Assessment Sourcebook

Includes multiple choice, constructed response, and writing items

Grade 4

- Placement Test
- Quick Check Masters
- Topic Tests
- Benchmark Tests
- End-of-Year Test
- Basic-Facts Timed Tests

Scott Foresman·Addison Wesley

enVisionMATH®
Common Core

PEARSON

Glenview, Illinois • Boston Massachusetts • Chandler, Arizona • Upper Saddle River, New Jersey

ISBN-13: 978-0-328-73135-0

ISBN-10: 0-328-73135-8

5 6 7 8 9 10   V011   19 18 17 16 15 14 13 12

Contents

Placement Test

Quick Check Masters
Topics 1–16

Topic Tests
Topics 1–16

Benchmark Tests
Topics 1–4
Topics 5–8
Topics 9–12
Topics 13–16

End-of-Year Test

Basic-Facts Timed Tests

Name_____

Mark the best answer.

1. Which number means the same as
80,000 + 5,000 + 600 + 20 + 5?

   A 8,005,625

   B 850,625

   C 805,625

   D 85,625

2. Look at the fraction model below.

   Which choice gives the unit
   fraction for each part of the whole
   and the fraction of the whole that
   is shaded?

   A $\frac{3}{4}$

   B $\frac{1}{8}, \frac{3}{8}$

   C $\frac{1}{6}, \frac{3}{6}$

   D $\frac{1}{4}, \frac{2}{4}$

3. Which list shows the numbers in
order from least to greatest?

   A 3,546; 3,654; 3,564

   B 3,564; 3,654; 3,546

   C 3,546; 3,564; 3,654

   D 3,654; 3,564; 3,546

4. Which shows 296 rounded to the
nearest ten?

   A 200

   B 290

   C 300

   D 310

5. What fraction is shown on the
number line?

   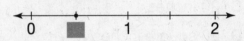

   A $\frac{1}{4}$

   B $\frac{1}{2}$

   C $\frac{3}{4}$

   D $1\frac{1}{4}$

6. The cafeteria sold 128 ham
sandwiches, 36 cheese
sandwiches, and 45 salads. About
how many sandwiches were sold?

   A 220

   B 190

   C 170

   D 130

Name_____

7. What is the perimeter of this shape?

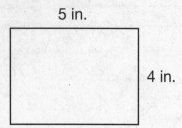

5 in.

4 in.

A 18 inches

B 18 square inches

C 20 inches

D 20 square inches

8. Last Saturday, Marge drove to the mountains. She drove 238 miles in the morning and 154 miles in the afternoon. How many more miles did she drive in the morning than in the afternoon?

A 392 miles

B 328 miles

C 124 miles

D 84 miles

9. Which is the best estimate of the mass of a small dog?

A 40 kilograms

B 4 kilograms

C 400 grams

D 40 grams

10. What is the area of this shape?

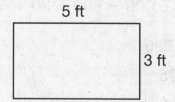

5 ft

3 ft

A 16 square feet

B 16 feet

C 15 square feet

D 15 feet

11. Which number sentence describes the stamps below?

A $3 + 4 = 7$

B $4 + 4 = 8$

C $3 \times 5 = 15$

D $3 \times 4 = 12$

12. Which fraction is equivalent to $\frac{6}{8}$?

A $\frac{4}{5}$

B $\frac{3}{4}$

C $\frac{2}{3}$

D $\frac{1}{2}$

Name_____

13. Miguel bought 2 bags of oranges. There are 8 oranges in each bag. Which number sentence shows how many oranges Miguel bought?

A $8 - 2 = 6$

B $8 + 2 = 10$

C $2 \times 8 = 16$

D $8 \div 2 = 4$

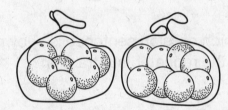

14. Carla is putting some pictures in an album. If she puts 6 pictures on each page, how many pictures are on 8 pages?

A 48 pictures

B 40 pictures

C 15 pictures

D 8 pictures

15. Look at the pictograph below. How many more students chose dogs as their favorite pets than cats?

Students' Favorite Pets	
Pets	Number of Votes
Cat	👤👤
Dog	👤👤👤👤
Fish	👤
Hamster	👤👤

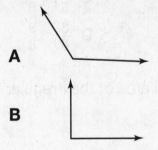

KEY: Each 👤 equals 3 students

A 4

B 6

C 12

D 18

16. Which of the following is a right angle?

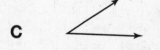

A

B

C

D

17. Which shape has four right angles and all sides equal in length?

A Rectangle   C Square

B Rhombus   D Trapezoid

18. Which of the following number sentences does **NOT** belong in the same fact family?

A $4 + 8 = 12$ C $32 \div 4 = 8$

B $4 \times 8 = 32$ D $32 \div 8 = 4$

19. Look at the number lines below.

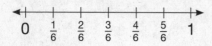

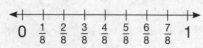

Which is a correct statement?

A $\frac{3}{6} = \frac{5}{8}$ C $\frac{3}{6} < \frac{5}{8}$

B $\frac{3}{6} > \frac{5}{8}$ D $\frac{3}{6} < \frac{3}{8}$

20. What is the area of the irregular figure?

A 20 square units

B 14 square units

C 12 square units

D 10 square units

21. How many wheels are on 4 wagons?

Wagons	Wheels
1	4
2	8
3	12
4	?

A 20   C 16

B 18   D 14

22. Which division sentence is shown by the repeated subtraction?

$27 - 9 = 18$
$18 - 9 = 9$
$9 - 9 = 0$

A $27 \div 9 = 4$

B $27 \div 9 = 3$

C $18 \div 2 = 9$

D $36 \div 4 = 6$

23. Which value for *b* will make the equation true?

$15 + b = 22$

A $b = 2$ C $b = 7$

B $b = 6$ D $b = 9$

24. Tom arrived for a meeting at 8:55 A.M. He was 25 minutes late for the start of the meeting. At what time did the meeting start?

A 8:45 A.M.   C 8:25 A.M.

B 8:30 A.M.   D 8:20 A.M.

1. Which of the following is the correct multiplication sentence for $4 + 4 + 4 + 4 + 4 + 4$?

   A $4 \times 4 = 16$

   B $2 \times 12 = 24$

   C $6 \times 4 = 24$

   D $8 \times 3 = 24$

2. Which of the following shows the correct array for a multiplication sentence for $3 + 3 + 3 + 3$.

   A

   B

   C

   D

3. **Writing to Explain** Draw an array using Xs and write a multiplication and an addition sentence you could use to show how 12 juice boxes could be arranged to form an array. Explain why they are both correct.

_____

_____

_____

Name_____

1. Skip count to find the number that comes next.
36, 45, 54, ____

   A 72

   B 63

   C 60

   D 55

2. Look at the display below. What is the product for this array?

   A 32

   B 40

   C 48

   D 56

3. **Writing to Explain** Seven people each brought two chairs to a family picnic. How many chairs will there be all together if another person does the same?

   _____

   _____

   _____

   _____

   _____

Name_____

1. Which property is best represented by the display below?

3 groups of 0

   A Zero Property of Multiplication

   B Commutative Property of Addition

   C Commutative Property of Multiplication

   D Identity Property of Multiplication

2. Which of the following is the missing number?

_____ $\times 6 = 6$

   A 6

   B 2

   C 1

   D 0

3. **Writing to Explain** What is the Commutative Property of Multiplication? Write a number sentence that shows this property.

_____

_____

_____

_____

Q1·3

Name_____

1. Use breaking apart to identify the missing number.

$3 \times 8 = (3 \times 4) + (3 \times \boxed{})$

A 1

B 2

C 4

D 6

2. Which is 1×4 broken apart?

A $(1 \times 2) + (1 \times 1)$

B $(1 \times 1) + (1 \times 2)$

C $(1 \times 2) + (1 \times 2)$

D $(2 \times 1) + (2 \times 2)$

3. Writing to Explain Use a grid to show 6×7 broken apart.

_____

_____

_____

_____

_____

_____

_____

_____

1. On Tuesday Danielle rode her bike to 2nd Street. On Wednesday she rode her bike to 4th Street. On Thursday she rode her bike to 6th Street. If the pattern continues, what street will she ride to on Saturday?

   A 8th Street

   B 10th Street

   C 12th Street

   D 14th Street

2. Jacob gave 3 toys to charity when he was five. He gave 6 toys away to charity when he was six, and he gave away 9 toys when he was seven. If the pattern continues, how many toys will he give away when he is ten?

   A 15

   B 18

   C 21

   D 30

3. There is a bus stop at 980 Main Street, 1030 Main Street, and 1080 Main Street. If the pattern continues, what will be the address of the next bus stop?

   A 1130 Main Street

   B 1140 Main Street

   C 1170 Main Street

   D 1200 Main Street

4. What is next in the pattern?

   $\uparrow, \rightarrow, \downarrow, \leftarrow, \uparrow, \rightarrow$

   A $\uparrow$

   B $\rightarrow$

   C $\downarrow$

   D $\leftarrow$

5. **Writing to Explain** The table shows how much money Oscar has in his savings. In which month will he have $390 in savings? Explain why.

Month	Savings
January	$30
February	$60
March	$90

_____

_____

Name_____

1. Yvette has 24 comics. She gives 6 comics to each of her friends. If she gives them all away, how many friends did she give comics to? Use the drawing to help you solve the problem.

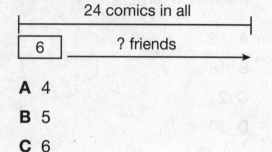

24 comics in all

6   ? friends

   A 4

   B 5

   C 6

   D 7

2. Jackson gives away all 42 of his comics to 6 friends. If each friend receives the same number, how many comics does each friend receive? Use the drawing to help you solve the problem.

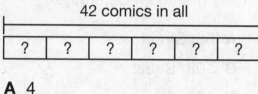

42 comics in all

? | ? | ? | ? | ? | ?

   A 4

   B 6

   C 7

   D 8

3. **Writing to Explain** Write a division problem that matches the drawing below. Explain your thinking.

60

? | ? | ? | ? | ?

_____

_____

_____

Name_____

1. Which number sentence below belongs in the fact family for 4, 5, and 20?

    A 4 + 5 = 20

    B 5 × 4 = 25

    C 20 ÷ 5 = 4

    D 20 − 5 = 4

2. Which choice shows a related multiplication and division sentence?

    A 2 × 5 = 10; 5 × 2 = 10

    B 81 ÷ 9 = 9; 9 × 8 = 72

    C 32 ÷ 8 = 4; 8 × 4 = 32

    D 35 ÷ 5 = 7; 25 ÷ 5 = 5

3. **Writing to Explain** The shapes below stand for whole numbers. What is the answer to the division problem? Explain how you found your answer.

 × =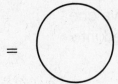

 ÷ = ?

_____

_____

_____

_____

1. For breakfast, 4 campers equally share 1 grapefruit that is divided into 4 sections. Which number sentence below shows the number of sections of grapefruit each camper will get?

   A $4 \div 4 = 1$

   B $4 \div 1 = 4$

   C $0 \div 4 = 0$

   D $8 \div 2 = 4$

2. There are 6 slices of cantaloupe. Jerome gave an equal number of slices of cantaloupe to his 6 friends. Which number sentence below shows the number of slices of cantaloupe each of his friends received?

   A $6 \div 6 = 1$

   B $6 \div 1 = 6$

   C $12 \div 1 = 12$

   D $12 \div 12 = 1$

3. Which number sentence shows how many people can have one slice of a pie that is divided into 8 slices?

   A $8 \div 8 = 1$

   B $8 \div 1 = 8$

   C $8 \div 4 = 2$

   D $8 \div 2 = 4$

4. **Writing to Explain** Luke has a foot-long sandwich that is cut into 6 pieces. How many people can have a piece of the sandwich? Write a number sentence to show how many people can have a piece of the sandwich. Explain your answer.

   _____

   _____

   _____

   _____

   _____

1. Jamal has 35 model airplanes in his collection. He displays his models on 7 shelves in his room. If there are an equal number of planes on each shelf, how many planes are displayed on each shelf?

A 5

B 7

C 28

D 42

2. Sandra ran a total of 14 miles last week. She ran every day. She ran the same number of miles each day. How many miles did she run each day?

A 28 miles

B 7 miles

C 2 miles

D There is not enough information to answer this question.

3. Lincoln bought 36 tomato plants. He planted an equal number of plants in 4 rows. How many plants are in each row?

A 6

B 7

C 8

D 9

4. Writing to Explain Write a multiplication sentence and a division sentence that represent the model below. Explain how you found your answer.

_____

_____

1. The United States flag had 25 stars in 1837. The flag has twice as many stars today. Which diagram shows how many stars the flag has today?

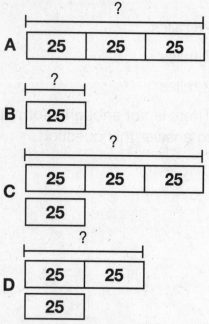

2. Kerry is watering her plants. The plant at her desk needs 5 times as much water as the plant by her window. The plant by her window needs 2 pints of water. How much water does the plant at her desk need?

   A 3 pints

   B 7 pints

   C 10 pints

   D 14 pints

3. Nina is 48 inches tall. Rafael is 53 inches tall. Which number sentence tells you how many inches taller Rafael is than Nina?

   A $48 + 53 = 101$

   B $101 - 53 = 48$

   C $53 + 5 = 58$

   D $53 - 48 = 5$

4. Ian is 6 years old. His brother Curtis is 3 times as old. Which number sentence tells you how old Curtis is?

   A $3 \times 6 = 18$

   B $3 \times 3 \times 3 = 27$

   C $3 + 3 + 3 = 9$

   D $9 \times 2 = 18$

5. **Writing to Explain** Adam's pet frog can jump 4 times as far as Sonya's. Sonya's frog can jump 8 inches. Draw a picture and write a number sentence to find how many inches Adam's frog can jump.

_____

_____

_____

1. What are the next three numbers in the pattern below?
6, 9, 1, 4, 6, 9, 1, 4, 6, 9, …

A 6, 9, 1

B 9, 1, 4

C 1, 4, 6

D 4, 6, 9

2. What are the next three symbols in the pattern below?

A

B

C

D

3. Cyndi is using shapes to make the pattern below. She wants the repeated part to appear 6 times in the finished pattern. How many stars will be in Cyndi's finished pattern?

♡ ☆ ☆ ♡ ☆ ☆ ♡ ☆

A 6

B 9

C 10

D 12

4. Writing to Explain Define a repeating pattern, and how you decide how to continue it. Then describe the 17th shape in the pattern below.

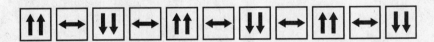

1. Which rule fits the pattern below?
   64, 56, 48, 40, ...

   A Add 6

   B Add 8

   C Subtract 6

   D Subtract 8

2. Rima used "add 3" as the rule to make a pattern. She started with 6, and wrote the next six numbers in her pattern. Which number does NOT belong in Rima's pattern?

   A 12

   B 14

   C 18

   D 21

3. Ivan counted all the beans in a jar. If he counted the beans in groups of 7, which list shows the numbers Ivan could have named?

   A 7, 14, 21, 24

   B 7, 14, 28, 54

   C 7, 14, 21, 28

   D 14, 24, 34, 44

4. **Writing to Explain** Use the rule "add 8" to make a pattern. Start with the number 75, and write the next 6 numbers. What is the meaning of the rule? Write about how you figured out the next numbers in the pattern. What number would come before 75 in this pattern?

Name_____

1. Look at the table.
   Which number replaces the ■?

Number of Boxes	1	2	5	■
Total Muffins	6	12	30	48

   A 6

   B 8

   C 9

   D 10

2. A squirrel travels about 12 miles in an hour. How far can it travel in 5 hours? Hint: Use a table.

   A 17 miles

   B 34 miles

   C 48 miles

   D 60 miles

3. This flower ✿ has 4 petals. How many total petals are there on 7 flowers like this? Hint: Use a table.

   A 11

   B 22

   C 28

   D 32

4. **Writing to Explain** A hockey game begins with 6 players for each team on the ice. How would you use a table to find out how many players would be on the ice if 6 teams played? Make a table, share your thinking, and give the answer.

1. Which is a rule for the table below?

Hours Worked	1	3	4	7
Money Earned	$7	$21	$28	$ ■

A Add 7

B Subtract 6

C Multiply by 7

D 49

2. Blake uses the rule "subtract 11" for her table.
If she starts with 50, what is the next number?

A 39

B 49

C 61

D 44

3. Writing to Explain Look at the table below. Write about how
you figure out a rule for the table. Then explain how to use
your rule to find the two missing numbers. Finally, make up a
pair of numbers that can go at the end of the table.

Earned	$21	$27	$12	$18	$33	
Saved	$7	$9		$6		

1. Wes made three block towers which are shown below.
   He recorded his pattern. If he continued the pattern,
   how many blocks would a 100-story tower have?

   A 200

   B 300

   C 500

   D 1,000

2. Lindy made three block towers which are shown below.
   The table shows her pattern. If she continued the pattern,
   how many blocks would the next tower have?

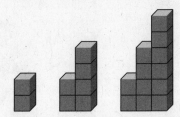

Number of Columns	1	2	3	4
Number of Blocks	2	6	12	?

   A 15

   B 16

   C 18

   D 20

3. **Writing to Explain** Look at the block towers in Exercise 2.
   Use grid paper to draw the fifth tower in the pattern. Explain
   the pattern in your own words. Tell how you know that your
   drawing is right.

Name_____

1. Jack has 9 coins in his pocket. He has only pennies and dimes. He has 3 fewer dimes than pennies. How much money does Jack have?

   A 63¢

   B 39¢

   C 36¢

   D 26¢

2. Tova has 17 marbles. The types of marbles she has are aggies, comets, and cat's eye. She has twice as many aggies as comets. She has 1 more cat's eye than comets. She has 8 aggies. How many cat's eyes does Tova have?

   A 4

   B 5

   C 9

   D 16

3. Aaron saw 27 animals at the circus. He saw 9 dogs, 6 elephants, and 3 camels. The rest of the animals were horses. Which expression shows one way to find the number of horses?

   A $27 - 9 - 6 + 3$

   B $27 + 9 + (6 \div 3)$

   C $27 - 9 - 6 - 3$

   D $6 \times 3 + 27 - 9$

4. **Writing to Explain** Solve the problem about toy cars below. Write about how you solved it. Explain your reasoning.

   Ana, Bea, and Cal collect toy cars. Ana has 6 more cars than Bea. Bea has 8 cars. They have 24 cars in all. How many cars does Cal have?

Name_____

1. A total of 57,429 people visited the boat museum last year. What is the value of the underlined number in 57,429?

   A 70

   B 700

   C 7,000

   D 70,000

2. Middletown has a population of 9,120. What is the word form of 9,120?

   A ninety-one thousand, twenty

   B nine thousand, twelve

   C nine thousand, one hundred two

   D nine thousand, one hundred twenty

3. How do you write 892,350 in expanded form?

   A 890,000 + 2,000 + 300 + 50

   B 800,000 + 90,000 + 2,000 + 300 + 50

   C 800,000 + 92,000 + 350

   D 800,000 + 90,000 + 1,000 + 1,000 + 300 + 50

4. Which of the following has a 3 in the ten thousands place?

   A 42,348

   B 53,402

   C 133,986

   D 376,909

5. **Writing to Explain** What is the greatest six-digit number you can write? What is the smallest six-digit number you can write? Draw two place-value charts and write one number in each place-value chart. Explain your answer.

   _____

   _____

1. Which of the following names the value of the 8s in 8,870?

   A 80 and 8

   B 800 and 8

   C 8,000 and 80

   D 8,000 and 800

2. In the number 5,332, the 3 in the hundreds place is _____ times greater than the 3 in the tens place.

   A three

   B ten

   C one hundred

   D one thousand

3. Which of the following shows a number with digits having the value of 60 and 6?

   A 4066

   B 4660

   C 6640

   D 4606

4. **Writing to Explain** What is the relationship between the values of the 4s in the number 4,438?

   _____

   _____

Name_____

1. Which number sentence is true if you replace the
   ■ with 34,625?

   A 35,624 > ■

   B 32,546 > ■

   C ■ = 32,654

   D ■ < 34,052

Use the table for **2** through **4**.

2. Which park listed in the table is
   the smallest?

   A Park A

   B Park B

   C Park C

   D Park D

Park	Size
Park A	30,784 acres
Park B	36,480 acres
Park C	21,000 acres
Park D	28,000 acres

3. Which number sentence shows that Park D is smaller than
   Park B?

   A 21,000 < 36,480

   B 28,000 < 36,480

   C 36,480 < 28,000

   D 28,000 = 28,000

4. **Writing to Explain** Tell how you know which park shown in
   the table is the largest.

   _____

   _____

   _____

   _____

1. Which of the following is the greatest number?

   A 90,786

   B 91,715

   C 90,864

   D 96,826

2. Which place value would you use to compare the numbers 14,321 and 11,941?

   A tens

   B hundreds

   C thousands

   D ten thousands

3. The table shows the totals for a Grade 4 reading contest.

Friend	Number of pages read
Nancy	5,062
Laurie	5,845
Pedro	4,929
Doug	4,026

   Which friend read the greatest number of pages?

   A Nancy

   B Laurie

   C Pedro

   D Doug

4. Which friend read the least number of pages?

   A Nancy

   B Laurie

   C Pedro

   D Doug

5. **Writing to Explain** When you compare the numbers on the left, you need to look at the ones digits. When you compare the numbers on the right, you do not need to compare the ones digits. Explain.

   5,278 5,272   5,398 5,353

_____

_____

Name_____

1. Round 85,3<u>8</u>6 to the place of the underlined digit.

   A 85,000

   B 85,380

   C 85,390

   D 85,400

2. Which number line shows 26,462 rounded to the nearest ten thousand?

   A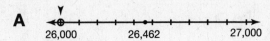

   B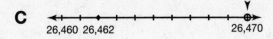

   C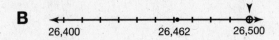

   D

3. **Writing to Explain** Use a number line to show how to round
   275,466 to the nearest ten thousand.

   _____

   _____

1. Jeff is ordering a soup and a sandwich. He can have split pea, bean, or noodle soup. He can have grilled cheese or a tuna sandwich. How many different soup and sandwich combinations can he have?

   A 2

   B 3

   C 6

   D 9

2. Tanya has blue, green, and yellow paper. She has black, brown, and gray pencils. How many paper and pencil combinations can she have?

   A 6

   B 9

   C 12

   D 15

3. Dylan wants to borrow a book and a CD from the library. How many book and CD combinations can he have?

Books	CDs
Lions	Bridges
Whales	Skyscrapers
Reptiles	Tunnels
	Trains

   A 12

   B 16

   C 20

   D 24

4. **Writing to Explain** Erin is thinking of a 3-digit number. It uses the digits 1, 7, and 4. How many numbers can you make that are even? How many numbers can you make that are odd? Explain your answers.

   _____

   _____

Name_____

1. 438 + 26

    A 412

    B 454

    C 464

    D 470

2. 532 − 167

    A 360

    B 365

    C 379

    D 699

3. 78 + 55

    A 123

    B 133

    C 145

    D 235

4. **Writing to Explain** Kevin wants to buy a new stereo for $239. So far, he has saved $115. Explain how you can use mental math to find out how much more money Kevin needs to save.

_____

_____

_____

1. The longest river in the world is the Nile River. It is 4,132 miles long. The longest river in the United States is the Missouri River. It is 2,540 miles long. Which is the best estimate of the difference in the lengths of the Nile and Missouri rivers?

   A 1,000 miles

   B 1,600 miles

   C 2,000 miles

   D 6,600 miles

2. Sue saved up $286. Then she received $75 for her birthday. About how much money does Sue have now?

   A $80

   B $300

   C $370

   D $500

3. **Writing to Explain** Zoe said the best way to estimate 2,498 − 639 is to round each number to the nearest hundred. Sam said the best way to estimate is to round each number to the nearest thousand. Who is correct? Explain your answer.

   _____

   _____

   _____

1. Juliana read 86 pages of her book last week. She read 58 pages of her book this week. How many pages of her book did she read in both weeks?

   A 171

   B 144

   C 32

   D 28

2. The third, fourth, and fifth grades collected aluminum cans for the recycling drive as shown in the table below. How many cans did they collect altogether?

Grade	Number of Cans Collected
Third	1,488
Fourth	1,872
Fifth	2,087

   A 3,360

   B 4,237

   C 5,407

   D 5,447

3. **Writing to Explain** Michael added the numbers 3,428 + 5,125. His work is shown below. His answer is not correct. Explain what he did wrong. Then, correctly answer the problem.

   $$\begin{array}{r} \overset{3}{}3,428 \\ +\ 5,125 \\ \hline 8,571 \end{array}$$

   _____

   _____

   _____

1. 559 − 381

    A 178

    B 228

    C 238

    D 940

2. 1,667 − 763

    A 840

    B 894

    C 904

    D 940

3. Hannah scored 5,772 points playing her favorite computer game. Joshua scored 4,881 points on the same game. How many more points did Hannah score than Joshua?

    A 891

    B 999

    C 1,001

    D 1,111

4. Writing to Explain Jeremy earned a total of $288 mowing lawns this summer. He plans to use the money he earned to buy a new bike. If the bike costs $279, how much money will Jeremy have left? Explain how you found your answer.

_____

_____

_____

_____

Circle the correct answer.

1. 408 − 259

    A 149

    B 151

    C 249

    D 251

2. 1,097 − 768

    A 239

    B 329

    C 1,031

    D 1,331

3. 9,070 − 4,675

    A 4,395

    B 4,415

    C 5,275

    D 5,605

4. **Writing to Explain** Petulia needed to subtract 375 from 700.
Is her answer correct? If not, explain why and write the correct answer.

$$\begin{array}{r} {\scriptstyle 9\,10} \\ 7\cancel{0}\cancel{0} \\ -375 \\ \hline 425 \end{array}$$

_____

_____

1. Raoul has 4 pennies and 5 dimes in his coat pocket. How many coins does he have in all?

   A 1

   B 9

   C 20

   D 45

2. Sofia picked 7 apples and gave 2 to Jules. How many apples does she have left?

   A 4

   B 5

   C 9

   D 14

3. Smallville is 104 miles east of Bigtown. Medburg is 206 miles east of Bigtown. How many miles is Medburg from Smallville?

   A 100 miles

   B 102 miles

   C 106 miles

   D 310 miles

4. **Writing to Explain** A model kit has 100 pieces. The kit has long beams, short beams, and connectors. There are 20 long beams and 30 short beams. Ann built a bridge from 62 pieces. How many pieces does she have left? Draw a picture to help you solve the problem.

   _____

   _____

Name_____

Circle the letter of the correct answer.

1. A shark has 3 rows of teeth. If the shark has 100 teeth in each row, how many teeth are there in all?

A   3

B   30

C 103

D 300

2. Ambika has 4 sheets of stickers. There are 10 stickers on each sheet. How many stickers does Ambika have?

A 400

B   40

C   14

D   4

3. Fred has 2 boxes of books. There are 10 books in each box. How many books does Fred have?

A 200

B 102

C   20

D   12

4. Jan bought 5 bags of shells. There are 100 shells in each bag. How many shells does Jan have?

A   50

B 105

C 500

D 501

5. Writing to Explain Miguel has 8 bags of marbles with 10 marbles in each bag. Pedro has 9 bags of marbles with 9 marbles in each bag. Who has more marbles? Explain how you know.

_____

_____

_____

_____

1. Amanda volunteers 9 hours a week at an animal shelter. If she volunteers 50 weeks a year, how many hours a year does she volunteer?

   A   45 hours

   B   450 hours

   C 4,500 hours

   D 45,000 hours

2. The number of students who attended an end-of-year school party was 6 times the number of students who are in the fourth grade. If there are 20 students in the fourth grade, how many students attended the party?

   A   120

   B   1,200

   C 12,000

   D 120,000

3. Use the basic multiplication fact $4 \times 4 = 16$ to solve 400×4.

   A 160,000

   B   16,000

   C   1,600

   D   160

4. **Writing to Explain** Use a basic multiplication fact to write a multiplication problem with 5,600 as the product. Explain your thinking.

   _____

   _____

   _____

   _____

Name_____

1. Which set of factors matches these partial products?

$3 \times 50 = 150$

$3 \times 7 = 21$

A 3 and 57

B 3 and 75

C 3 and 50 and 7

D 3 and 171

2. What is the product of 4×65?

A 270

B 260

C 250

D 249

3. Randy is counting the books on 7 shelves. Each shelf has 148 books. Which number sentence shows how to use breaking apart to find the total number of books on the shelves?

A $148 + 7$

B $148 - 7$

C $(7 \times 1) + (7 \times 4) + (7 \times 8)$

D $(7 \times 100) + (7 \times 40) + (7 \times 8)$

4. **Writing to Explain** What is a partial product? Describe how you would find partial products to multiply 4×36. Then give the product.

_____

_____

_____

_____

Name_____

Use the table for Exercises **1** through **3**.

Item	Cost
T-shirt	$14
Sweatshirt	$28
Jacket	$113

1. Coach Anderson wants to buy each member of his swim team a sweatshirt. If there are 9 members on the team, how much will Coach Anderson spend?

   A $180

   B $252

   C $270

   D $288

2. Six members of the swim team decide to order T-shirts. How much do they spend on T-shirts all together?

   A $116

   B $104

   C $96

   D $84

3. Seven members of the swim team decide to buy jackets. How much do they spend in all?

   A $791

   B $678

   C $226

   D $113

4. **Writing to Explain** Damien used the method below to find the product of 291 × 9. What did Damien do wrong? What is the correct answer? Explain your reasoning.

   291 × 10 = 2,910

   2,910 − 9 = 2,901

   So, 291 × 9 = 2,901.

   _____

   _____

1. There are 61 fourth-grade students at Lincoln Elementary School. Each fourth-grader brought in 5 cans for the recycling drive. About how many cans did the fourth-graders collect?

   A About 600

   B About 500

   C About 400

   D About 300

2. There are 189 fifth- and sixth-grade students at Lincoln Elementary. Each of those students brought in 6 cans. About how many cans did they collect in all?

   A About 600

   B About 1,000

   C About 1,200

   D About 2,000

3. **Writing to Explain** Use rounding to estimate the product 12 × 9. Then, use compensation to find the actual answer. If Alison was rounding to find the total cost for 12 books that were $9 each, would she get a good estimate? Explain.

   _____

   _____

   _____

   _____

Name_____

1. Ursula has an album in which she keeps pressed flowers. The album has 34 pages, and each page has 7 pressed flowers. Which of the following shows a reasonable estimate of how many pressed flowers Ursula has?

A $30 \times 7 = 210$

B $40 \times 7 = 280$

C $50 \times 5 = 250$

D $60 \times 4 = 240$

2. Isabelle has 9 ant farms. Each ant farm has 99 ants. Which of the following shows a reasonable estimate of how many ants Isabelle has?

A $7 \times 125 = 875$

B $8 \times 110 = 880$

C $9 \times 100 = 900$

D $10 \times 100 = 1,000$

3. At an athletic club there are 11 people on a sports team. There are 8 teams. About how many people are on teams?

A About 80

B About 70

C About 50

D About 20

4. Kenny has 7 pouches. Each pouch has 21 marbles. About how many marbles does Kenny have?

A 200

B 140

C 100

D 70

5. Writing to Explain Every day for 1 week Derek's cousin told him 11 jokes. Each joke took 3 minutes to tell. Derek thinks his cousin told him 33 minutes of jokes in the 1 week. Explain why this answer is not reasonable.

_____

_____

Name_____

1. Which numbers complete the calculation?

$$
\begin{array}{r}
27 \\
\times\ 6 \\
\hline
+ \\
\hline
\end{array}
$$

A 42, 120, 162

B 13, 127, 140

C 42, 112, 154

D 27, 120, 147

2. Which array represents 4×19?

A

B

C

D

3. Lilly caught a small sailfish that weighed 29 pounds. Sue caught a sailfish that weighed 4 times as much as Lilly's. To find the weight of Sue's sailfish, Lilly multiplied 29×4. What partial products can be used to find the weight of Sue's sailfish?

A 8 and 6

B 36 and 8

C 80 and 36

D 83 and 6

4. Writing to Explain Gerard listened to his favorite song 26 times a week for 4 weeks. How many times did he hear his favorite song in 4 weeks? Explain how you can use partial products to find the answer.

_____

_____

_____

_____

Q 6·1

Name_____

1. Each table in the cafeteria at Mario's school seats 16 children. How many children can be seated at 4 tables if there are no empty seats?

   A 50

   B 64

   C 74

   D 80

2. Jerri needs to buy new pastels. She picks sets with 36 different colors. How many new pastels will she have if she buys 5 new sets?

   A 150

   B 180

   C 185

   D 300

3. A flower shop sells many kinds of bouquets. Below is part of a bouquet chart.

Type	Stems Used
Assorted	15
Daisies	24
Roses	12

   How many stems are needed for 7 bouquets of daisies?

   A 168

   B 167

   C 151

   D 118

4. Tim is multiplying 36 by 7. Which are the two partial products he would add to find the product?

   A 42 and 12

   B 42 and 80

   C 42 and 100

   D 42 and 210

5. **Writing to Explain** Cara drew the following diagram to solve a multiplication problem. Explain how Cara could solve this problem using the expanded algorithm and the standard algorithm.

   ? in all

48	48	48

   ↑
   Number in
   each group

1. Julia has 4 bookshelves. Each bookshelf has 56 books. How many books does Julia have?

   A 224

   B 200

   C 44

   D 24

2. David plays a baseball game 18 times a month. How many times does he play baseball in 3 months?

   A 243

   B 64

   C 54

   D 21

3. Ken hosts a radio show 6 times a week. He hosts the show 49 weeks a year. Which shows the most reasonable estimate of the number of times Ken hosts the show in one year?

   A $5 \times 40 = 200$

   B $5 \times 50 = 250$

   C $6 \times 40 = 240$

   D $6 \times 50 = 300$

4. A factory can make 52 toys an hour. The factory is open for 8 hours a day. How many toys does the factory make in 1 day?

   A 56

   B 400

   C 416

   D 432

5. **Writing to Explain** What is the greatest product possible when you multiply a 1-digit number greater than 0 by a 2-digit number? What is the least product possible when you multiply a 1-digit number greater than 0 by a 2-digit number?

   _____

   _____

   _____

1. A freight company is shipping 3 pianos that weigh 1,117 pounds each. How much do the 3 pianos weigh in all?

   A 3,501 pounds

   B 3,361 pounds

   C 3,351 pounds

   D 3,312 pounds

2. Luke has 6 boxes of baseball cards. Each box has 213 cards. How many cards does he have?

   A 198

   B 639

   C 1,224

   D 1,278

3. A pet store has 9 large fish tanks. In each fish tank there are 423 fish. How many fish are in all the fish tanks?

   A 3,600

   B 3,645

   C 3,807

   D 3,825

4. Members of a book club each read a 1,296-page book. There are 7 members in the club. How many pages did the book club members read in all?

   A 9,072

   B 9,054

   C 8,582

   D 8,043

5. **Writing to Explain** Martin multiplied 423 by 7 and found an incorrect answer of 2,841. What did Martin do wrong? What is the correct answer? Explain what Martin needs to do to find the correct answer.

   _____

   _____

   _____

Name_____

1. A large cruise ship can carry 2,348 passengers. How many passengers can travel in all if the cruise ship makes 5 trips and is full each time?

A 11,630

B 11,740

C 12,300

D 12,540

2. Frank multiplied 7 and 528 and got the product 3,696. Which estimate shows that his answer is reasonable?

A $5 \times 500 = 2,500$

B $5 \times 600 = 3,000$

C $7 \times 500 = 3,500$

D $7 \times 600 = 4,200$

3. The Schillers buy 4 new chairs that cost $199 each for their dining room. What is the total cost of the four chairs?

A $800

B $798

C $796

D $696

4. A small theater has 99 seats. A play is being performed 8 times at that theater. If each performance is sold out, how many people will be able to see the play?

A 722

B 747

C 782

D 792

5. Writing to Explain Mr. Teal orders the same business lunch for 5 people. Everyone has a salad for $5, a steak sandwich for $12, lemonade for $3, and dessert for $4. He adds in a tip of $3 for each person. What is the total cost of the 5 lunches? Show your work.

_____

_____

_____

Name_____

1. Ben drove 4,212 miles. Larry drove 3,400 miles. Ben drove at a speed of about 55 miles per hour. How many more miles does Ben drive than Larry?

   A 406 miles

   B 812 miles

   C 4,212 miles

   D Not enough information

2. The Patton family has 8 members. The Smith family has 3 members. A movie ticket costs $9, and a large popcorn costs $6 at the local theater. How much more does it cost the Patton family to buy movie tickets than it does the Smith family?

   A $72

   B $45

   C $24

   D Not enough information

3. Aidan, Collin, and Laura collect stamps. Aidan has 114 stamps. Laura has twice as many stamps. How many stamps does Collin have?

   A 116 stamps

   B 200 stamps

   C 214 stamps

   D Not enough information

4. **Writing to Explain** Yolanda is putting up a fence for her dog in the shape of a square. Each foot of fencing costs $7. She plans to make each side of the fence 12 feet long. Explain whether you have enough information to find the number of feet of fencing Yolanda needs.

   _____

   _____

Name_____

1. The dentist ordered 10 boxes of toothbrushes. There are 15 toothbrushes in each box. How many toothbrushes did the dentist order? Use the array to help.

   A   25

   B   100

   C   150

   D 1,500

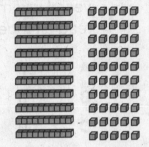

2. Margaret walks 30 minutes every day. How many minutes does she walk in a month that has 31 days? Use the array to help.

   A 930 minutes

   B 901 minutes

   C 300 minutes

   D   61 minutes

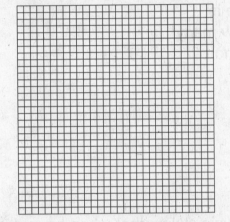

3. **Writing to Explain** Draw an array to show how to find 30 × 23. Then explain how you can use the array to find the product.

   _____

   _____

   _____

   _____

1. Every day, 60 people eat at Franco's Diner. How many people eat there in 30 days?

A 2,000

B 1,800

C 180

D 90

2. Each of the 90 fourth-grade students at North Elementary read 30 books over the school year. How many books did they read all together?

A 27

B 270

C 2,700

D 27,000

3. One centimeter is equal to 10 millimeters. If a photo is 10 centimeters long, how many millimeters long is the photo?

A 10,000 millimeters

B 1,000 millimeters

C 100 millimeters

D 10 millimeters

4. Writing to Explain Dominic claims that when he multiplied 40 × 50 he got an answer of 200. Is Dominic correct? Explain why or why not.

_____

_____

_____

_____

Name_____

1. Meg saves $38 each week from the money she earns working part time. What is the best estimate of how much Meg will save in 52 weeks?

   A $150

   B $1,500

   C $2,000

   D $2,500

2. Carl volunteers about 32 hours each month at the local hospital. What is the best estimate of how many hours he volunteers in 12 months?

   A 600 hours

   B 300 hours

   C 40 hours

   D 32 hours

3. It took Anne 18 hours to drive from her home to Miami. She drove about 62 miles each hour. Which shows the best way to estimate the distance from Anne's home to Miami?

   A 60 × 10

   B 60 × 20

   C 70 × 10

   D 70 × 20

4. Andy is stacking 49 boxes of paper on the shelves of an office supply store. Each box weighs about 28 pounds. What is the best estimate of the total weight of the boxes?

   A 80 pounds

   B 1,000 pounds

   C 1,200 pounds

   D 1,500 pounds

5. **Writing to Explain** Describe how you could use rounding to estimate the product of 38 × 42.

_____

_____

_____

_____

1. A park ranger takes 24 groups of people hiking each week. There are 32 people in each group. What is the best estimate of how many people hike with the park ranger each week?

   A 1,000

   B   750

   C   500

   D   400

2. A toy store ordered 26 crates of stuffed bears. There are 21 stuffed bears in each crate. What is the best estimate of how many stuffed bears the store ordered?

   A 1,000

   B   900

   C   500

   D   400

3. The puppies at an animal shelter are exercised 25 minutes a day. Which is the best way to use compatible numbers to estimate how many minutes the puppies were exercised in 42 days?

   A 25×50

   B 25×40

   C 20×40

   D 25×30

4. A science museum shows a movie about dinosaurs 24 times each week. There are 44 seats in the movie theater. What is the best estimate of how many people can watch the movie each week?

   A   100

   B   500

   C   700

   D 1,000

5. **Writing to Explain** Describe how you could use compatible numbers to estimate the product of 37×24.

   _____

   _____

   _____

   _____

1. Fourteen students in Ms. Engel's class have 2 pets. Three students have 1 pet. There are 3 students that do not have any pets. How many pets does the class have all together?

   A 3

   B 20

   C 23

   D 31

2. The gym teacher has 4 yoga tapes. She has 3 times as many dance tapes as yoga tapes. How many yoga and dance tapes does she have in all?

   A 43

   B 34

   C 16

   D 12

3. Aspen is setting up chairs for a concert. One section will have 5 equal rows of 5 chairs each. The other section will have 8 equal rows of 2 chairs each. How many chairs will there be in all?

   A 41

   B 36

   C 35

   D 20

4. Rose has 18 pictures of birds. She has half as many pictures of trees as pictures of birds. She has 3 times as many pictures of flowers as trees. How many pictures of birds, trees, and flowers does Rose have?

   A 9

   B 27

   C 18

   D 54

5. **Writing to Explain** A tennis pro has 12 cans of tennis balls. There are 3 balls in each can. He gives an equal number of balls to each of 4 players. After the lesson, he realizes that each player lost 3 balls. How many tennis balls are left? Show your work and explain how you found your answer.

   _____

   _____

   _____

1. Each of the 27 students in Mr. Moro's class brought in 18 aluminum cans during the class recycling drive. How many aluminum cans did Mr. Moro's class collect in all?

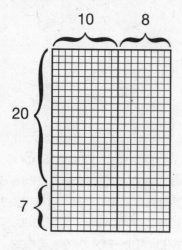

A 476

B 486

C 586

D 596

2. There are 27 students in Mrs. Langley's class. Each student does 15 math homework problems each night. How many math problems in all does the class do in one night?

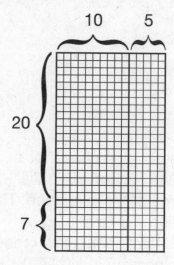

A 405

B 305

C 300

D 255

3. Writing to Explain Molly had the following work on her paper:

	40	2
80	3,200	160
6	240	12

What multiplication problem is Molly trying to solve? How do you know?

_____

_____

_____

Name_____

1. Noriko multiplies 13 × 45. Which of the following is NOT a partial product?

   A 15

   B 50

   C 90

   D 400

2. One table in the school cafeteria can seat 12 students. How many students can be seated at 18 tables?

   A 216

   B 206

   C 144

   D 54

3. The table lists three types of photo albums for sale at PhotoWorld and the number of pictures each album can hold.

Album Type	Number of Pictures
Brag Book	16
Party Album	32
Mega-Memories	75

   Mrs. Kudan buys 11 Brag Books. How many pictures will it take to fill all of the albums?

   A 176

   B 123

   C 96

   D 27

4. **Writing to Explain** Use the diagram at the right to explain how you could use it to find 22 × 14. List the partial products and then solve.

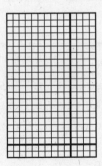

1. Marla drinks 74 ounces of water a day. How much water does she drink over 40 days?

   A 2,860 ounces

   B 2,880 ounces

   C 2,960 ounces

   D 2,980 ounces

2. Lincoln can type 58 words a minute. How many words can he type in one hour?

   A 3,420

   B 3,480

   C 3,980

   D 4,980

3. 17 students each brought in 20 cookies for the school bake sale. How many cookies were there at the bake sale?

   A 400

   B 380

   C 360

   D 340

4. **Writing to Explain** Use a grid to find the product of 30 × 29. Then, explain how you can use a grid to find the partial products and the product.

   _____

   _____

   _____

   _____

1. Jacob reads 68 pages each night. How many pages does Jacob read in a month with 31 days?

   A 2,108

   B 2,208

   C 2,618

   D 2,868

2. Mrs. Jackson has had 24 students in her class every year. How many students has she taught in her 22 years of teaching?

   A 628

   B 620

   C 538

   D 528

3. Which partial products can be used to find the product shown below?

   $$\begin{array}{r} 51 \\ \times\ 42 \\ \hline \end{array}$$

   A 2 and 2,000

   B 10 and 2,400

   C 12 and 2,040

   D 102 and 2,040

4. Find the product.

   $$\begin{array}{r} 76 \\ \times\ 18 \\ \hline \end{array}$$

   A 684

   B 1,368

   C 1,468

   D 1,768

5. **Writing to Explain** How is using partial products to find the product of a 2-digit by 2-digit problem similar to how you have used partial products in the past? How is it different?

   _____

   _____

   _____

1. Doug spent 16 days at summer camp. Each day he spent 4 hours at arts and crafts. Each hour at arts and crafts he made 3 drawings. How many drawings did he make while at summer camp?

   A 192

   B 112

   C 48

   D 12

2. Margo has 8 different kinds of tea in her pantry. Each kind of tea is in a different box, and there are 14 packets of tea in each box. Her friend Liz has the same number of tea packets. How many tea packets do they have in all?

   A 112

   B 168

   C 224

   D 448

3. Mr. Rivera teaches 6 classes per day. Each class has 15 students. After school, he coaches the baseball team. There are 12 students on the baseball team that do not have a class with him. How many students does Mr. Rivera work with each day?

   A 90

   B 102

   C 162

   D 180

4. There are 22 tables in the cafeteria. Each table can seat 8 students. There are 4 lunch periods each day. How many students can the cafeteria seat each day?

   A 822

   B 704

   C 264

   D 176

5. **Writing to Explain** Ernie spends 6 hours reading each weekend. Ernie has 3 sisters. Each sister reads the same amount Ernie does each weekend. How many hours do Ernie and his sisters read in all?

   _____

   _____

1. Sandra has 350 rocks she has collected. She displays her rocks on 7 shelves in her room. If there are an equal number of rocks on each shelf, how many rocks are on each shelf?

   A 50

   B 70

   C 280

   D 420

2. James's dad drove a total of 140 miles last week. He drove the same number of miles each day and he drove every day. How many miles did he drive each day?

   A 280 miles

   B 70 miles

   C 20 miles

   D 10 miles

3. **Writing to Explain** Use patterns of zeros to find $5{,}600 \div 7$. Show your work and explain your answer.

   _____

   _____

   _____

   _____

   _____

   _____

1. Jake likes to count stars. In 5 nights, Jake counted 354 stars. About how many stars did he count each night?

   A About 50

   B About 70

   C About 90

   D About 100

2. Melissa's father can type very fast. He typed 445 words in 5 minutes. About how many words did he type per minute?

   A About 200 words per minute

   B About 150 words per minute

   C About 100 words per minute

   D About 90 words per minute

3. Writing to Explain Seven pages of a school newspaper contain 628 words. About how many words are on each page? Explain how you found your answer.

_____

_____

_____

_____

_____

Estimate each quotient.

1. 186 ÷ 8

    A 20

    B 30

    C 200

    D 300

2. 6,983 ÷ 8

    A 80

    B 90

    C 800

    D 900

3. A beekeeper harvested enough honey to fill 224 jars.
He packs the jars into boxes with 6 jars in each box.
How many boxes does he need?

    A 30

    B 40

    C 300

    D 400

4. Writing to Explain Mrs. Rhee has a box containing
233 photographs. She plans to put them in an album.
If she can place 6 photographs on each page, about how
many pages will she need? Will the actual number of pages
be more or less than your estimate? How do you know?

_____

_____

_____

1. Ken has taken 85 pictures, and he needs to put them into an album. If each page holds only 9 pictures, and there are 9 pages in the album, how many pictures will be left out?

   A 67

   B 49

   C 6

   D 4

2. Robert jogged for a total of 67 minutes on the treadmill. If he jogged 8 times, about how many minutes did he jog each time on the treadmill?

   A 8 minutes

   B 9 minutes

   C 67 minutes

   D 75 minutes

3. **Writing to Explain** Curtis's mother drives the soccer team to practice. She can take 5 people on each ride. If there are 14 students on the soccer team, how many trips will Curtis's mother have to make? Explain how you found your answer.

   _____

   _____

   _____

   _____

Name_____

1. Ben's mother is driving the soccer team to their game. Her car can fit 6 players. There are 14 players on the soccer team. How many trips must Ben's mother make to drive everyone to the game?

   A 2

   B 3

   C 8

   D 20

2. Ms. Hill divided the fourth graders into groups of 7. If there are 45 fourth graders, how many are not yet in a group?

   A 6

   B 5

   C 4

   D 3

3. **Writing to Explain** Write a division problem and a multiplication problem that matches the model shown below. Explain your thinking.

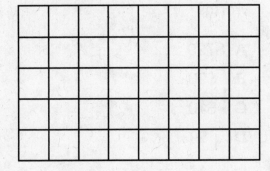

_____

_____

_____

_____

1. Mr. Perkins has 18 songs. He has an equal number of rockabilly songs, country songs, and rock songs. How many of each kind of song does he have?

   A 21

   B 20

   C 6

   D 3

2. Lee has 72 golf balls. He has 9 colors of golf balls with an equal number of each color. Which number sentence shows how many of each color he has?

   A $9 \div 1 = 9$

   B $9 \div 9 = 1$

   C $72 \div 9 = 8$

   D $72 + 9 = 81$

3. Carl is planting seeds. He has 36 seeds that he wants to plant in 6 rows. Which shows the number of seeds that will go into each row?

   A
   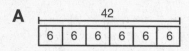

   B
   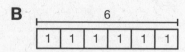

   C
36					
6	6	6	6	6	6

   D
36					
1	2	3	4	5	6

4. Shauna has an art collection. She has 9 paintings that are each worth the same amount. The total amount the paintings are worth is $81. How much is each painting worth?

   A $729

   B $90

   C $10

   D $9

5. **Writing to Explain** There are 48 people invited to Jill's graduation dinner. At dinner, 8 people will sit at each table. How many tables will there be? Draw a picture to explain your answer.

_____

_____

_____

1. Mr. Johnson counted 20 people who carpool to work. A total of 5 people will fit into each car. How many cars will they need? Use counters and repeated subtraction to help you solve the problem.

   A 4

   B 5

   C 6

   D 7

2. Jackson gives away all 42 of his comics to friends. If he gives 6 comics to each friend, how many friends will he give comics to? Use counters and repeated subtraction to help you solve the problem.

   A 4

   B 6

   C 7

   D 8

3. **Writing to Explain** Explain how to solve the following problem using counters and repeated subtraction.

   Rachel has 40 stickers and wants to place 8 stickers in each pile. How many piles of 8 stickers can she make?

   _____

   _____

   _____

1. Yusef picked 24 flowers. He put 4 flowers in each vase. How many vases did Yusef need? Use the drawing to help you solve the problem.

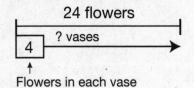

24 flowers

4   ? vases

↑
Flowers in each vase

A 2

B 4

C 6

D 8

2. Jon has 32 trading cards. He puts the cards into piles of 8 cards. How many piles does he make? Use the drawing to help you solve the problem.

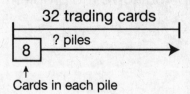

32 trading cards

8   ? piles

↑
Cards in each pile

A 3

B 4

C 6

D 7

3. **Writing to Explain** Linda's family has 30 mittens in their winter closet. Explain how you can record division as repeated subtraction to find out how many pairs of mittens Linda's family has.

_____

_____

_____

Name_____

1. Anya is putting her 70 baseball
cards into piles. There are 5 cards
in each pile with no cards left over.
How many piles did Anya make?

   A 5

   B 14

   C 19

   D 21

2. Mrs. Dryson is dividing her
collection of 52 glass bears into
groups of equal numbers. She has
1 bear left over. How many groups
did Mrs. Dryson make?

   A 17

   B 16

   C 10

   D 9

3. Writing to Explain Carla used the place-value blocks shown
to solve a division sentence.

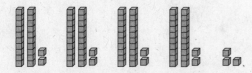

What is the division sentence that Carla solved?
Explain how you know.

_____

_____

_____

1. Mark is reading a book with 96 pages. It takes him 4 days to read the book. He reads the same number of pages each day. How many pages does Mark read each day?

A 14

B 18

C 24

D 28

2. Celia has 83 beads. She makes 6 bracelets and uses the same number of beads for each bracelet. How many beads does Celia have left over?

A 5

B 4

C 3

D 0

3. Writing to Explain Jessica solved the division problem as shown.

$$
\begin{array}{r}
13 \\
7\overline{)95} \\
-7 \\
\hline
25 \\
-21 \\
\hline
4
\end{array}
$$

The answer is 17.

Is her answer correct? If not, what did Jessica do wrong? How could she have checked her work?

_____

_____

_____

1. In one week, the Evanston Recycling Center received 784 aluminum cans. They received the same number of cans each day. How many cans did the recycling center receive each day?

   A 112

   B 114

   C 121

   D 122

2. Zoe is helping her parents at their store, The Sock Stop. She is organizing 658 pairs of socks into display boxes. Each display box holds 4 pairs of socks. How many pairs of socks are left over?

   A 3

   B 2

   C 1

   D 0

3. **Writing to Explain** There are 786 people at Dorothy's Diner. Five people can sit at a table. How many tables are in Dorothy's Diner? How many people cannot sit at one of the tables? Explain.

   _____

   _____

   _____

1. Lucy has a card-making business. She has an order to make 65 cards in 8 days. She makes the same number of cards each day for 7 days. How many cards does she have to make on the 8th day?

   A 0

   B 1

   C 2

   D 3

2. A shipment of 8 boxes just arrived at Litman's Bookstore. Each box holds the same number of books. If there are 744 books in the shipment, how many books are in each box?

   A 193

   B 103

   C 93

   D 90

3. **Writing to Explain** Which of the following problems will have 3-digit quotients? How do you know?

   a. 2)‾621   **b.** 3)‾152   **c.** 4)‾912

   d. 5)‾734   **e.** 6)‾452   **f.** 6)‾529

   _____

   _____

   _____

Estimate. Then find each quotient. Use your estimate to check if your answer is reasonable.

1. Sam's father has an orchard of grapefruit trees. He has 3,429 trees that are arranged in 9 equal rows. What is 3,429 ÷ 9?

   A 340

   B 381

   C 400

   D 441

2. Ron's Tire Corral has 1,767 tires for heavy-duty trucks. Each heavy-duty truck needs 6 tires. How many trucks could get all new tires at Ron's, and how many tires would be left?

   A 280 trucks, 5 tires left

   B 291 trucks, 0 tires left

   C 294 trucks, 3 tires left

   D 300 trucks, 1 tire left

3. **Writing to Explain** Explain how you would estimate the answer to the problem shown below. Then check to see if your estimate is close to the actual quotient.

   > In 8 days, a hair salon gave 1,536 haircuts. The salon gave the same number of haircuts each day. How many haircuts did the hair salon give each day?

   _____

   _____

   _____

1. Zoe's recipe calls for 1 pound of walnuts. She has 4 pounds of walnuts. How many extra pounds of walnuts does Zoe have?

   A 1 pound

   B 2 pounds

   C 3 pounds

   D 4 pounds

2. Jorge wants to buy carpet for his living room and bedroom. His living room is 30 square yards and his bedroom is 21 square yards. If carpet costs $12 a square yard, how much will it cost to carpet these rooms?

   A $612

   B $562

   C $360

   D $252

3. **Writing to Explain** Find the hidden question in the problem below and explain why it's the hidden question.

   Sheila bought four bags of apples and three bags of pears from the market. Each bag of apples cost $2 and each bag of pears cost $3. She paid with a twenty dollar bill. How much change did she receive?

   _____

   _____

   _____

Name_____

1. Sal has 13 stamps arranged in an array. Which of the following shows an array he could use?

   A 13×2

   B 1×13

   C 2×7

   D 3×4

2. Danna has 39 coins. She wants to display them in an array. Which of the following describes all of the arrays she can make?

   A 1 by 39

   B 3 by 13, 13 by 3

   C 1 by 39, 3 by 13

   D 1 by 39, 39 by 1, 3 by 13, 13 by 3

3. A store has 45 cans of soup. The store manager wants to display the soup in an array. Which of the following shows 3 ways the soup could be displayed?

   A 1 by 9, 9 by 5, 3 by 15

   B 15 by 3, 9 by 1, 5 by 9

   C 5 by 9, 3 by 15, 9 by 5

   D 45 by 1, 15 by 1, 9 by 1

4. **Writing to Explain** Mr. Deets is making an array to display 16 pictures. For each pair of different factors, there are two arrays he can make. How many different arrays can he make? Is the number odd or even? Explain.

   _____

   _____

   _____

   _____

1. Kyle has 17 toy trucks. How many ways can the trucks be placed in equal groups?

   A 5 ways

   B 4 ways

   C 3 ways

   D 2 ways

2. The number of candles Sabrina has is a prime number. Which expression shows the number of ways she can group her candles if c represents the number of candles?

   A $c \times 1, 1 \times c$

   B $c \times 1$

   C $1 \times c, 17 \times c$

   D $17 \times c, c \times 1$

3. At a marina there are 51 boats. How many ways can the boats be placed in equal groups?

   A 2 ways

   B 4 ways

   C 8 ways

   D 16 ways

4. **Writing to Explain** Larry says that all numbers that have a 2 in the ones place are composite numbers. Explain why Larry would say that and if his rule is correct or incorrect.

   _____

   _____

   _____

1. Latifa and John played a game of multiples. Each player picks a number card and says a multiple of that number. Latifa picked a 9. Which number is a multiple of 9?

   A 17

   B 29

   C 37

   D 45

2. A roller-coaster ride completes a full loop every 3 minutes. Sven listed multiples of 3 to find when the ride would be back to its starting point. Which are multiples of 3?

   A 3, 6, 9, 12, 15

   B 3, 13, 23, 33, 43

   C 3, 9, 15, 21, 25

   D 1, 2, 3, 6, 9

3. In which pair of numbers is the first number a multiple of the second number?

   A 38, 4

   B 27, 9

   C 32, 6

   D 24, 5

4. Which number is NOT a multiple of 6?

   A 12

   B 18

   C 23

   D 42

5. **Writing to Explain** What is the least multiple the numbers 6 and 8 have in common? Explain how you found your answer.

   _____

   _____

   _____

Name_____

1. Which fraction is equivalent to $\frac{6}{8}$?

    A $\frac{2}{4}$

    B $\frac{3}{5}$

    C $\frac{3}{4}$

    D $\frac{5}{6}$

2. Which picture shows a fraction equivalent to $\frac{1}{6}$?

A

B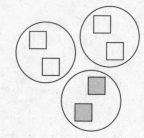

C

D

3. Writing to Explain Use fraction strips to show $\frac{1}{3}$, $\frac{2}{6}$, and one whole. Do $\frac{1}{3}$ and $\frac{2}{6}$ name the same part of one whole?

_____

_____

_____

In **1** and **2**, use the number line below to find the best answer.

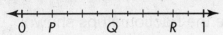

1. Which two fractions name point P on the number line?

   A $\frac{3}{4}$ or $\frac{9}{12}$

   B $\frac{1}{2}$ or $\frac{3}{6}$

   C $\frac{2}{6}$ or $\frac{4}{12}$

   D $\frac{1}{6}$ or $\frac{2}{12}$

2. Which two fractions name point R on the number line?

   A $\frac{5}{6}$ or $\frac{1}{12}$

   B $\frac{10}{12}$ or $\frac{5}{6}$

   C $\frac{3}{4}$ or $\frac{4}{6}$

   D $\frac{2}{6}$ or $\frac{1}{3}$

3. About $\frac{3}{4}$ of the earth's surface is water. Which of the following fractions names the same point on the number line?

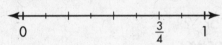

   A $\frac{3}{8}$

   B $\frac{4}{8}$

   C $\frac{5}{8}$

   D $\frac{6}{8}$

4. **Writing to Explain** A recipe calls for $\frac{1}{4}$ cup of flour. Carter does not have a quarter-cup measuring cup, though he has a measuring cup that holds $\frac{1}{8}$ cup. Draw a number line to show a fraction equivalent to $\frac{1}{4}$. How can Carter use this equivalent fraction to measure the flour he needs for his recipe?

_____

_____

_____

Name_____

1. Use the fraction strips shown. Which choice shows a correct comparison?

1			
$\frac{1}{4}$	$\frac{1}{4}$	$\frac{1}{4}$	$\frac{1}{4}$
$\frac{1}{8}$ $\frac{1}{8}$	$\frac{1}{8}$ $\frac{1}{8}$	$\frac{1}{8}$ $\frac{1}{8}$	$\frac{1}{8}$ $\frac{1}{8}$

A $\frac{3}{8} < \frac{3}{4}$

B $\frac{3}{4} < \frac{3}{8}$

C $\frac{1}{8} > \frac{1}{4}$

D $\frac{1}{4} > \frac{3}{8}$

2. Use the fraction strips shown. Which choice shows a correct comparison?

1		
$\frac{1}{3}$	$\frac{1}{3}$	$\frac{1}{3}$
$\frac{1}{6}$ $\frac{1}{6}$	$\frac{1}{6}$ $\frac{1}{6}$	$\frac{1}{6}$ $\frac{1}{6}$

A $\frac{1}{3} < \frac{1}{6}$

B $\frac{3}{6} < \frac{1}{3}$

C $\frac{4}{6} > \frac{3}{6}$

D $\frac{2}{3} < \frac{4}{6}$

3. **Writing to Explain** Which fraction is greater, $\frac{4}{5}$ or $\frac{4}{8}$? Use words and draw models to explain your answer.

_____

_____

_____

_____

_____

_____

_____

Name_____

1. Which of the following shows fractions in order from least to greatest?

A $\frac{1}{2}, \frac{3}{4}, \frac{7}{8}$

B $\frac{4}{5}, \frac{1}{3}, \frac{2}{8}$

C $\frac{3}{4}, \frac{6}{8}, \frac{1}{8}$

D $\frac{3}{6}, \frac{2}{6}, \frac{1}{6}$

2. Which of the following shows fractions in order from greatest to least?

A $\frac{1}{4}, \frac{2}{4}, \frac{3}{4}$

B $\frac{3}{8}, \frac{1}{4}, \frac{3}{4}$

C $\frac{3}{4}, \frac{2}{3}, \frac{5}{10}$

D $\frac{1}{6}, \frac{1}{3}, \frac{1}{2}$

3. Writing to Explain Use equivalent fractions to order these fractions from least to greatest: $\frac{2}{3}, \frac{1}{2}, \frac{4}{12}, \frac{5}{6}$. Explain the steps you took to find your answer.

_____

_____

_____

_____

_____

_____

1. While testing 10 light bulbs, Harvey finds that 6 of them do not light. Which best describes the fraction of light bulbs that are working?

   A number of light bulbs that are not working/total number of light bulbs

   B number of light bulbs that are working/number of light bulbs not working

   C number of light bulbs that are not working/number of light bulbs working

   D number of light bulbs that are working/total number of light bulbs

2. Timmy weighs 85 pounds. This is 5 times as much as his bicycle. Which of these models would you use to explain how much Timmy's bicycle weighs?

   A
   | 85 lb |
   | B | B | B | B | B |

   B
   | weight of bicycle |
   | 85 | 85 | 85 | 85 | 85 |

   C
   | 85 lb |
   | B | B | B | B | B | B | B | B |

   D
   | weight of bicycle |
   | 85 | 85 | 85 | 85 | 85 | 85 | 85 | 85 |

3. **Writing to Explain** Ted is building a brick patio with red and gray bricks. He uses a pattern in which the number of red bricks increases by two as the number of gray bricks increases by one. When Ted has 5 gray bricks, how many red bricks will he need? Draw a diagram and explain.

   _____

   _____

Name_____

In **1** through **3**, use fraction strips to add. Simplify if possible.

1. $\frac{1}{12} + \frac{3}{12} + \frac{5}{12}$

A $\frac{5}{6}$

B $\frac{3}{4}$

C $\frac{7}{12}$

D $\frac{1}{2}$

2. There are 10 players in a soccer club. Three of the players are in fifth grade. Five of the players are in sixth grade. What fraction of the players are in fifth and sixth grade?

A $\frac{1}{4}$

B $\frac{1}{2}$

C $\frac{2}{3}$

D $\frac{4}{5}$

3. **Writing to Explain** The table shows the distances David hiked on each day of a camping trip.

Day	Distance
Thursday	$\frac{1}{8}$ mile
Friday	$\frac{2}{8}$ mile
Saturday	$\frac{2}{8}$ mile
Sunday	$\frac{3}{8}$ mile

How far did David hike Thursday and Friday? _____

How far did David hike Saturday and Sunday? _____

How far did David hike during his camping trip? _____

Show your work.

_____

_____

_____

Name_____

Add the fractions. Simplify, if possible.

1. $\frac{2}{12} + \frac{3}{12} + \frac{1}{12}$

    A $\frac{3}{12}$

    B $\frac{1}{2}$

    C $\frac{3}{4}$

    D $\frac{5}{6}$

2. Rosa has $\frac{3}{10}$ of a yard of red ribbon and $\frac{2}{10}$ of a yard of blue ribbon. How much red and blue ribbon does she have?

    A $\frac{1}{2}$ of a yard

    B $\frac{3}{5}$ of a yard

    C $\frac{4}{5}$ of a yard

    D $\frac{9}{10}$ of a yard

3. Writing to Explain An ice cream shop has four different shake flavors: chocolate, vanilla, strawberry, and banana. One day, $\frac{3}{10}$ of the shakes they sold were chocolate, $\frac{4}{10}$ were vanilla, $\frac{1}{10}$ were strawberry, and $\frac{2}{10}$ were banana.

Chocolate $\frac{3}{10}$ Vanilla $\frac{4}{10}$ Strawberry $\frac{1}{10}$ Banana $\frac{2}{10}$

What fraction of the shakes sold were strawberry or chocolate? What fraction were chocolate, vanilla, or strawberry? Show your work.

_____

_____

_____

Name_____

In **1** through **3**, use fraction strips to find each difference.
Simplify, if possible.

1. $\frac{9}{12} - \frac{5}{12}$

  A $\frac{1}{4}$

  B $\frac{1}{3}$

  C $\frac{5}{12}$

  D $\frac{14}{12}$

2. $\frac{4}{5} - \frac{3}{5}$

  A $\frac{7}{5}$

  B $\frac{7}{10}$

  C $\frac{2}{5}$

  D $\frac{1}{5}$

3. Ellen divides a piece of fabric into 8 equal sections by drawing chalk lines. Then she cuts 5 of the sections off to make into placemats. What fraction of the fabric is left?

  A $\frac{2}{8}$

  B $\frac{3}{8}$

  C $\frac{4}{8}$

  D $\frac{5}{8}$

4. Writing to Explain Michael had $\frac{8}{10}$ of a pound of raisins. He used $\frac{3}{10}$ of a pound of raisins to make trail mix. What fraction of a pound of raisins does he have left? Draw fraction strips to show how you solved the problem.

_____

_____

Name_____

In **1** through **3**, find each difference.
Simplify if possible.

1. $\frac{7}{10} - \frac{3}{10}$

   A 1

   B $\frac{4}{5}$

   C $\frac{1}{2}$

   D $\frac{2}{5}$

2. $\frac{7}{12} - \frac{5}{12}$

   A $\frac{1}{12}$

   B $\frac{1}{6}$

   C $\frac{1}{2}$

   D $\frac{12}{12}$

3. Of the fifth graders at Oak Elementary, $\frac{6}{8}$ are in band. What fraction of the fifth-grade students are NOT in band?

   A $\frac{1}{4}$

   B $\frac{3}{8}$

   C $\frac{1}{2}$

   D $\frac{5}{8}$

4. **Writing to Explain** Darin completed $\frac{1}{8}$ of his homework before dinner and $\frac{5}{8}$ of his homework after dinner. What fraction of his homework does he have left to complete? Explain how you got your answer.

_____

_____

_____

_____

_____

1. Which equation is represented on the number line?

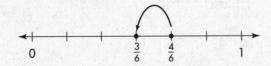

A $\frac{4}{6} - \frac{1}{6} = \frac{3}{6} = \frac{1}{2}$

B $\frac{4}{6} + \frac{1}{6} = \frac{5}{6}$

C $\frac{4}{6} - \frac{1}{6} = \frac{2}{6}$

D $\frac{4}{6} + \frac{1}{6} = \frac{6}{6} = 1$

2. Which equation is represented on the number line?

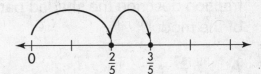

A $\frac{2}{5} - \frac{1}{5} = \frac{1}{5}$

B $\frac{2}{5} - \frac{1}{5} = \frac{3}{5}$

C $\frac{2}{5} + \frac{1}{5} = \frac{3}{10}$

D $\frac{2}{5} + \frac{1}{5} = \frac{3}{5}$

3. Which number line illustrates the following problem?

To get to his grandmother's house, Juan ran $\frac{3}{8}$ of a mile. Then he walked $\frac{2}{8}$ of a mile. How far is it to his grandmother's house?

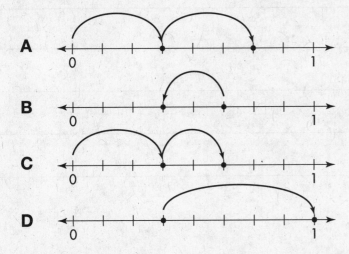

4. **Writing to Explain** Alex hiked $\frac{6}{12}$ of a trail; then he stopped to have a snack. Then he hiked another $\frac{4}{12}$ of the trail; then he stopped to rest. What fraction of the trail had Alex hiked when he stopped to rest? Draw a number line and explain how you found your answer. Simplify your answer.

1. Look at the model below. Which mixed number and improper fraction describe the shaded part of the model?

A $3\frac{3}{4}$; $\frac{15}{4}$

B $4\frac{1}{4}$; $\frac{15}{4}$

C $4\frac{3}{4}$; $\frac{6}{4}$

D $3\frac{1}{4}$; $\frac{6}{4}$

2. Which choice below shows the improper fraction $\frac{11}{3}$ written as a mixed number?

A $4\frac{1}{3}$

B $3\frac{2}{3}$

C $2\frac{1}{2}$

D $2\frac{1}{3}$

3. Writing to Explain Write the mixed number $4\frac{1}{2}$ as an improper fraction. Draw a model and explain your thinking.

_____

_____

_____

_____

Name_____

For **1** through **3**, use fraction strips to find each sum or difference.

1. What is the sum of $6\frac{7}{8} + 4\frac{5}{8}$?

   A $10\frac{1}{8}$

   B $10\frac{1}{2}$

   C $11\frac{1}{2}$

   D $11\frac{5}{8}$

2. What is the difference of $5\frac{1}{5} - 2\frac{3}{5}$?

   A $2\frac{3}{5}$

   B $2\frac{1}{2}$

   C $1\frac{4}{5}$

   D $1\frac{3}{5}$

3. Lou used $3\frac{1}{8}$ cups of oats and $1\frac{3}{8}$ cups of raisins in a recipe. How many more cups of oats did Lou use than raisins?

   A $1\frac{1}{4}$ more cups

   B $1\frac{3}{4}$ more cups

   C $4\frac{1}{2}$ more cups

   D $5\frac{1}{2}$ more cups

4. Writing to Explain Use the models of mixed numbers below to answer **a** and **b**.

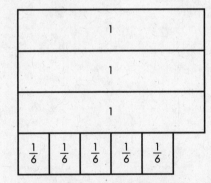
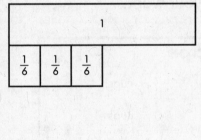

  a Write a mixed number for each model.

  b Explain how you can use the models to find how much greater one mixed number is than the other.

1. What is the sum of $4\frac{2}{5}$ and $2\frac{3}{5}$?

  A $6\frac{2}{5}$

  B 7

  C $7\frac{1}{5}$

  D $7\frac{4}{5}$

2. Find the sum of $3\frac{3}{8} + 1\frac{1}{8}$.

  A $3\frac{4}{8}$

  B $4\frac{3}{8}$

  C $4\frac{1}{2}$

  D $5\frac{1}{4}$

3. Mr. Romano walks $1\frac{7}{8}$ miles from his home to the train station. Then he takes the train $9\frac{5}{8}$ miles to work. How many total miles does Mr. Romano travel to get to work?

  A $11\frac{1}{2}$

  B $11\frac{3}{8}$

  C $10\frac{3}{4}$

  D $10\frac{1}{8}$

4. Writing to Explain A recipe calls for bread flour and whole-wheat flour. What is the total amount of flour used in the recipe? Express your answer as a mixed number in simplest form. Show your work.

Recipe	
bread flour	$1\frac{9}{12}$ cups
whole-wheat flour	$1\frac{8}{12}$ cups
milk	1 cup
water	2 cups
sugar	$1\frac{3}{12}$ cups
yeast	2 tablespoons

_____

_____

Name_____

1. What is the difference of $6\frac{1}{5} - 1\frac{4}{5}$?

   A $4\frac{2}{5}$

   B $4\frac{3}{5}$

   C $5\frac{2}{5}$

   D $5\frac{3}{5}$

2. Find the difference of $8\frac{1}{6} - 4\frac{5}{6}$.

   A $3\frac{1}{6}$

   B $3\frac{2}{6}$

   C $4\frac{1}{6}$

   D $4\frac{2}{6}$

3. Some of the largest insects are beetles. The Titanus beetle can measure $16\frac{7}{10}$ centimeters in length and the Giant Weta beetle can measure $8\frac{5}{10}$ centimeters in length. How much longer is the Titanus than the Giant Weta?

   A $25\frac{1}{5}$ centimeters

   B $9\frac{1}{5}$ centimeters

   C $8\frac{2}{3}$ centimeters

   D $8\frac{1}{5}$ centimeters

4. **Writing to Explain** Jessie is building a doghouse. For one side of the roof, she needs a board that is $7\frac{9}{12}$ feet long. She has a board that measures $9\frac{1}{12}$ feet. How much of the length does she need to cut from the board? Show your work.

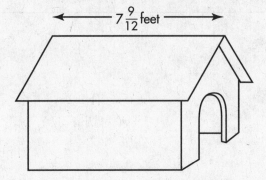

$7\frac{9}{12}$ feet

_____

_____

Name_____

Answer the questions below.

1. What is another way to show $\frac{1}{4} + \frac{3}{4}$?

   A $\frac{1}{4} + \frac{1}{4} + \frac{1}{4}$

   B $\frac{1}{2} + \frac{1}{4}$

   C $\frac{3}{4} + \frac{3}{4}$

   D $\frac{2}{4} + \frac{1}{4} + \frac{1}{4}$

2. What is another way to show $\frac{3}{12} + \frac{5}{12} + \frac{7}{12}$?

   A $\frac{4}{12} + \frac{4}{12} + \frac{4}{12} + \frac{3}{12}$

   B $\frac{11}{12}$

   C $1 + \frac{3}{4}$

   D $\frac{1}{12} + \frac{1}{12} + \frac{1}{12} + \frac{1}{12} + \frac{1}{12}$

3. **Writing to Explain** Ethan used $\frac{7}{8}$ cup of white rice and $\frac{6}{8}$ cup of brown rice. How much rice did Ethan use in all? Suppose Ethan has three other types of rice—long grain, short grain, and jasmine rice. What is another way he can combine these three types of rice to equal the total of the white and brown rice? Draw fraction strips to show your answer.

_____

_____

Name_____

For **1** and **2**, you may draw a picture and write an equation to help.

1. Betty mixed $\frac{1}{6}$ pound of peanuts with $\frac{2}{6}$ pound of raisins.
   How much mix did Betty have in all?

   A $\frac{1}{4}$ pound   **C** $\frac{1}{2}$ pound

   B $\frac{1}{3}$ pound   **D** 1 pound

2. Jill exercised for $1\frac{1}{3}$ hour. She did aerobics for $\frac{2}{3}$ hour and
   then lifted weights the rest of the time. How long did Jill lift
   weights?

   A $\frac{2}{3}$ hour   **C** $\frac{1}{3}$ hour

   B $\frac{4}{5}$ hour   **D** $\frac{1}{5}$ hour

3. Justin used $\frac{1}{4}$ pound of broccoli to make a stir-fry and $\frac{2}{4}$ pound
   of broccoli to make cheddar and broccoli soup. Which picture
   can be used to find how much broccoli Justin used in all?

   A 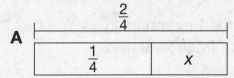   **C**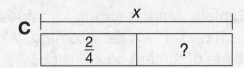

   B 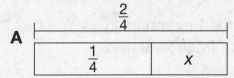   **D**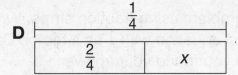

4. **Writing to Explain** Matt jogged $\frac{4}{8}$ of a mile. Thomas jogged $\frac{5}{8}$ of a mile. How
   much farther did Thomas jog? Draw a picture and write an equation to solve.

   _____

   _____

1. Which multiplication equation describes the fraction on the number line below?

    A $6 = \frac{6}{8} \times \frac{1}{8}$

    B $\frac{6}{8} = 6 \times \frac{1}{8}$

    C $\frac{1}{8} = \frac{1}{8} \times 6$

    D $\frac{1}{8} + 6 = \frac{6}{8}$

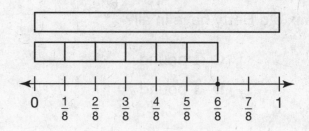

$$0 \quad \frac{1}{8} \quad \frac{2}{8} \quad \frac{3}{8} \quad \frac{4}{8} \quad \frac{5}{8} \quad \frac{6}{8} \quad \frac{7}{8} \quad 1$$

2. Which multiplication equation describes the picture below?

    A $\frac{3}{3} = 3 \times 1$

    B $\frac{3}{2} = 3 \times 1\frac{1}{2}$

    C $\frac{3}{1} = 3 \times \frac{1}{2}$

    D $\frac{3}{2} = 3 \times \frac{1}{2}$

3. **Writing to Explain** Mark is slicing tomatoes for 4 members in his family. Each person will eat $\frac{1}{3}$ tomato. What fraction shows how many thirds of tomato he will slice?

    Model the problem using fraction strips. Write your answer as a multiplication equation with $\frac{1}{3}$ as a factor. Draw your model and explain how you found your answer.

    _____

    _____

    _____

    _____

1. Which multiplication equation goes with the picture?

   A $3 \times \frac{1}{8} = \frac{3}{8}$

   B $3 \times \frac{2}{8} = \frac{6}{8}$

   C $4 \times \frac{2}{8} = \frac{6}{8}$

   D $6 \times \frac{2}{8} = \frac{12}{8}$

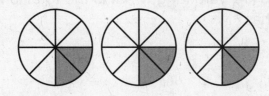

2. Justine feeds her dog $\frac{3}{4}$ cup of dog food each day. Which multiplication equation shows how much dog food she needs to feed her dog for one week?

   A $7 \times \frac{3}{4}$ cup $= \frac{10}{4}$ cups

   B $7 \times \frac{3}{4}$ cup $= \frac{14}{4}$ cups

   C $7 \times \frac{3}{4}$ cup $= \frac{21}{4}$ cups

   D $7 \times \frac{3}{4}$ cup $= \frac{28}{4}$ cups

$\frac{3}{4}$	$\frac{3}{4}$	$\frac{3}{4}$	$\frac{3}{4}$	$\frac{3}{4}$	$\frac{3}{4}$	$\frac{3}{4}$

3. **Writing to Explain** Gabe is making 5 capes. He uses $\frac{2}{3}$ yard of fabric for each cape he makes. What is the total amount of fabric Gabe needs? Use the diagram at the right. Show your answer as a multiplication equation of a whole number and a fraction. Explain.

$\frac{2}{3}$	$\frac{2}{3}$	$\frac{2}{3}$	$\frac{2}{3}$	$\frac{2}{3}$

   _____

   _____

   _____

   _____

1. Xander has 10 pieces of twine that he is using for a project. If each piece of twine is $\frac{1}{3}$ yard long, what is the total length of twine that Xander has?

    A 3 yards

    B $3\frac{1}{3}$ yards

    C $3\frac{2}{3}$ yards

    D 4 yards

2. Juliette is making 15 salads. She puts $\frac{2}{5}$ cups of carrots in each salad. What is the total amount of carrots Juliette will use?

    A 3 cups

    B $3\frac{2}{5}$ cups

    C 6 cups

    D $15\frac{2}{5}$ cups

3. **Writing to Explain** Oscar wants to make 4 chicken pot pies. The recipe for 1 chicken pot pie calls for $\frac{2}{3}$ of a pound of potatoes. What is the total amount of potatoes that Oscar will need? Explain.

    _____

    _____

    _____

    _____

1. Which fraction and decimal does the model represent?

   ▨▨▨▨▨▨□□□

   A $\frac{7}{10}$, 0.7

   B $\frac{7}{100}$, 0.07

   C $\frac{7}{7}$, 1.0

   D $\frac{70}{1}$, 70.0

2. Which is $\frac{1}{5}$ as a decimal?

   A 0.10

   B 0.20

   C 0.40

   D 0.50

3. **Writing to Explain** Draw a decimal model and write 0.78 as a fraction in simplest form.

_____

Name_____

1. Which fraction represents the location of point *Q*?

   A $\frac{3}{10}$

   B $\frac{4}{10}$

   C $\frac{2}{5}$

   D $\frac{3}{5}$

2. Which decimal represents the location of point *Z*?

   A 0.09

   B 0.01

   C 0.9

   D 0.8

3. **Writing to Explain** Draw a number line. Draw and label points to show the locations of $\frac{5}{10}$ and 0.7. Explain your answer.

_____

_____

_____

Name_____

1. Which shows $\frac{3}{12}$ as a decimal?

   A 0.025

   B 0.25

   C 0.312

   D 0.35

2. Which shows a pair of equivalent numbers?

   A $\frac{16}{20}$; 0.8

   B $\frac{25}{100}$; 0.4

   C $\frac{6}{8}$; 0.68

   D $\frac{3}{5}$; 0.75

3. Which shows $\frac{9}{20}$ as a decimal?

   A 0.92

   B 0.55

   C 0.45

   D 0.092

4. Which shows a pair of equivalent numbers?

   A $\frac{4}{5}$; 0.45

   B $\frac{3}{100}$; 0.3

   C $\frac{15}{20}$; 0.8

   D $\frac{3}{50}$; 0.06

5. **Writing to Explain** When writing $\frac{3}{6}$ as a decimal, why do you first need to rename the fraction as $\frac{1}{2}$ and then as $\frac{5}{10}$?

_____

_____

_____

1. A mail-order company shipped a package that weighed 73.87 pounds. What is the place value of the underlined digit in 73.8<u>7</u>?

   A hundredths

   B tenths

   C ones

   D tens

2. What is the standard form of eighty-four and twenty-seven hundredths?

   A 0.8427

   B 8.427

   C 84.27

   D 842.7

3. The average score for the high school golf team was 76.9. What is the word form of 76.9?

   A seven hundred and sixty-nine hundredths

   B seven and sixty-nine tenths

   C seventy-six and nine tenths

   D seventy-six and nine hundredths

4. What is the value of the point on the number line below?

   A 0.826

   B 8.26

   C 8.62

   D 86.2

5. **Writing to Explain** Rosa is thinking of a number between 9.04 and 9.15 that has a 6 in the hundredths place. What is the number? Explain.

   _____

   _____

   _____

Name_____

1. Which of the following is the greatest number?

   A 9.92

   B 9.82

   C 9.83

   D 9.81

2. Which place value would you use to compare the numbers 61.02 and 61.12?

   A tens

   B ones

   C tenths

   D hundredths

3. The table shows how far from school four friends live.

Friend	Distance from School in Miles
Ned	4.62
Jack	4.24
Paula	4.21
André	4.66

   Which friend lives the greatest distance from school?

   A Ned

   B Jack

   C Paula

   D André

4. Which friend lives the least distance from school?

   A Ned

   B Jack

   C Paula

   D André

5. **Writing to Explain** In a science lab, Ping measured the mass of three minerals:

   8.18 grams, 8.28 grams, 8.2 grams

   Explain how Ping should order the measures from greatest to least.

   _____

   _____

   _____

1. Laura earns $6.70 a week walking dogs. How much is that in dollars and dimes?

    A 6 dollars and no dimes

    B 6 dollars and 7 dimes

    C 6 dollars and 70 dimes

    D 67 dollars and no dimes

2. How many pennies more than two dollars are there in $2.05?

    A zero

    B two

    C five

    D ten

3. Which is equal to 3 dollars, 7 dimes, and 2 pennies?

    A $2.37

    B $3.72

    C $7.23

    D $72.30

4. Which is equal to $8.45?

    A 8 dollars, 4 dimes, 5 pennies

    B 8 dollars, 45 dimes

    C 84 dollars, 5 pennies

    D 84 dollars, 5 dimes

5. Which of the following has the greatest value?

    A 1 dollar, 4 dimes, 8 pennies

    B 1 dollar, 3 dimes, 11 pennies

    C 1 dollar, 3 dimes, 8 pennies

    D 1 dollar, 2 dimes, 27 pennies

6. Writing to Explain Barbara has 11 dimes. Evan has 1 dollar. Who has more money? Explain.

_____

_____

_____

Name_____

1. Which decimal represents the location of point *A*?

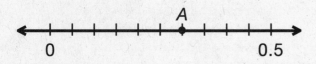

A 0.1

B 0.2

C 0.3

D 0.4

2. Which decimal represents the location of point *Z*?

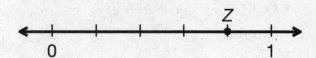

A 0.9

B 0.8

C 0.6

D 0.3

3. The following points were labeled on a number line: 0.30, 0.45, 0.60. What is the relationship between each point?

A Increase by 0.2

B Each point is twice the value of the preceding one

C Each point is the same distance apart

D Each point is $\frac{1}{2}$ that of the preceding point

4. Writing to Explain Draw a number line. Draw and label points to show the locations of 0, 0.25, 0.5, 0.75, and 1. Explain how the points relate to each other.

_____

_____

_____

Name_____

1. Which unit would you most likely use to measure the length of a desktop?

    A inch

    B yard

    C foot

    D mile

2. What is the measure of the line below to the nearest inch?

    A 1 in.

    B 3 in.

    C 2 in.

    D 4 in.

3. Writing to Explain Would you use yards to measure the height of a door? Explain.

_____

_____

_____

1. Which unit would be best to use to measure the capacity of a large fish tank?

   A cup

   B gallon

   C quart

   D pint

2. Which unit would be best to use to measure the capacity of a can of fruit juice?

   A cup

   B gallon

   C quart

   D pint

3. **Writing to Explain** What would be a good way to measure the capacity of a swimming pool? Should you use cups, pints, quarts, or gallons? Explain your answer.

   _____

   _____

   _____

1. Which unit of measure would be best to use to measure the weight of a small hammer?

    A pounds

    B ounces

    C liters

    D tons

2. Which shows the best estimate for the weight of a car?

    A 2,000 ounces

    B 2,000 tons

    C 2,000 pounds

    D 2,000 pints

3. **Writing to Explain** Would you use ounces, pounds, or tons to measure the weight of a laptop computer? Explain.

    _____

    _____

    _____

    _____

Name_____

1. Rose is told by her athletic trainer to drink 8 cups of water a day. How many quarts is that?

   A 0.5 qt

   B 1 qt

   C 2 qt

   D 4 qt

2. A loaf of bread requires 16 ounces of flour. How many pounds of flour does it take to bake 10 loaves of bread?

   A 15 lb

   B 13 lb

   C 10 lb

   D 8 lb

3. Jeff was $\frac{1}{4}$ of his way home from school. How many feet away from his house was he if the distance from his home to school was 812 feet?

   A 103 feet

   B 203 feet

   C 808 feet

   D 3,248 feet

4. **Writing to Explain** David helps his dad with grocery shopping. He wants to buy Brand X or Brand Y ground beef. He knows his dad wants the best value, so he compares the prices. 48 oz of Brand X is $6. 4 lbs of Brand Y is $12. Which brand is the better value? Show your work and explain your answer.

   _____

   _____

   _____

   _____

1. The height of Ali's robot is 22 inches. Michael's robot is 6 inches taller than Ali's robot. Which is the height of Michael's robot?

   A 5 feet 4 inches

   B 3 feet 6 inches

   C 4 feet 11 inches

   D 2 feet 4 inches

2. Erin used 9 ounces of fruit in the pie she baked. Nicole baked two pies and used 11 more ounces of fruit than Erin. Which is the amount of fruit that Nicole used?

   A 4 ounces

   B 1 pound

   C 1 pound 4 ounces

   D 1 pound 6 ounces

3. **Writing to Explain** Sam is 4 feet 5 inches tall. Karolyn is half a foot shorter. Karolyn's mom, Meredith, is two feet taller than Karolyn. Explain how to find each person's height in inches.

   _____

   _____

1. Which would be most appropriate to measure the distance of an airplane ride?

   A kilometers

   B centimeters

   C meters

   D millimeters

2. What is the measure of the pen to the nearest centimeter?

   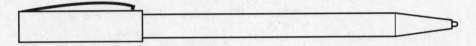

   A 10 cm

   B 14 cm

   C 12 cm

   D 16 cm

3. **Writing to Explain** What would be the best unit of metric measure to use to measure the width of a green bean? Explain.

   _____

   _____

   _____

Name_____

1. About how many milliliters of water would fill the thimble shown?

   A 8 liters

   B 10 milliliters

   C 20 milliliters

   D 30 milliliters

2. Which shows the best estimate of how many liters of water it would take to fill a bathtub?

   A 1,000 liters

   B 150 liters

   C 50 liters

   D 10 liters

3. **Writing to Explain** Ruth and Ben each measured the capacity of an aquarium. Ben measured the capacity in liters, and Ruth measured the capacity in milliliters. Which student's measurement had the highest number? Explain your answer.

   _____

   _____

   _____

1. Choose the correct word to complete the sentence below.
   Mass is the measure of the amount of ____ in an object.

   A space

   B weight

   C matter

   D volume

2. Which choice below shows the best estimate for the mass of
   a typical spoon?

   A 1 gram

   B 10 grams

   C 1 kilogram

   D 50 grams

3. **Writing to Explain** One pound is about 450 grams. About
   how many grams is 12 pounds? Show your work and explain
   your answer.

   _____

   _____

   _____

1. Juana drinks $\frac{1}{4}$ liter of water with every meal. How many milliliters of water will she drink in three meals?

    A 250 mL

    B 500 mL

    C 750 mL

    D 1,000 mL

2. A large zucchini has a mass of about $\frac{1}{2}$ kg. About how many grams of mass will 4 large zucchinis have?

    A 2,000 g

    B 1,000 g

    C 500 g

    D 2 g

3. Roger walked $\frac{1}{2}$ kilometer from his home to a park. Then he walked 200 meters in the park, and walked home. How far did he walk altogether?

    A 300 m

    B 1,200 m

    C 1,800 m

    D 3,000 m

4. **Writing to Explain** Margo says there is less than 1 meter in 270 kilometers. Is she correct? Why or why not?

_____

_____

_____

1. It took Lois 20 weeks to hike the Appalachian Trail. How many months did it take her?

   A 3 months

   B 4 months

   C 5 months

   D 6 months

2. Carter is 11 years old. His sister is 13 months younger than him. How many months old is his sister?

   A 156 months

   B 145 months

   C 132 months

   D 119 months

3. Mrs. Cash teaches 8 classes a day. Each class is 45 minutes long. How many hours does Mrs. Cash teach each day?

   A 6

   B 8

   C 60

   D 360

4. **Writing to Explain** John wants to find the age of everyone in his family in months.

John's Family		
Family Member	**Age**	**Age in Months**
John's father	4 decades	
John's mother	38 years	
John's brother	180 days	
John	500 weeks	

Fill in the table and explain which operation you used to change each age into months.

1. Laurie has band practice at 10:15 A.M. It takes her 20 minutes to get from home to practice and 5 minutes to warm up. What time should she leave home to get to practice on time?

   A 9:50 A.M.

   B 9:55 A.M.

   C 10:00 A.M.

   D 10:10 A.M.

2. Eunice has a soccer game at 7:00 P.M. She needs to be there 20 minutes early to warm up for the game, and it takes her 45 minutes to get to the soccer field. What time should she leave her house?

   A 5:55 P.M.

   B 6:05 P.M.

   C 6:15 P.M.

   D 6:40 P.M.

3. **Writing to Explain** Janice takes 20 minutes to get dressed for school. She eats breakfast for 30 minutes more, then walks to school. It takes Janice 15 minutes to walk to school. Janice needs to be at school by 8:55 A.M. What time is the latest she should get out of bed in the morning?

   _____

   _____

   _____

1. Find the length of the rectangle.

   A 10 in.

   B 20 in.

   C 27 in.

   D 70 in.

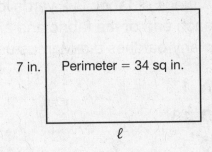

7 in. | Perimeter = 34 sq in.

ℓ

2. Find the length of the rectangle.

   A 4 mi

   B 8 mi

   C 21 mi

   D 30 mi

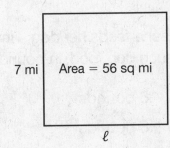

7 mi | Area = 56 sq mi

ℓ

3. A bulletin board is 3 feet high. Its area is 15 square feet. What is the perimeter of the bulletin board?

   A 3 ft

   B 8 ft

   C 16 ft

   D 36 ft

4. **Writing to Explain** Nassim wants to build a kitchen table with a top that has an area of 20 square feet. If the length and width must be whole numbers, how could he find all the possible dimensions of the table top? How would he decide which pair of dimensions makes the most sense for a table?

_____

_____

_____

_____

Name_____

Name_____

1. A piece of fabric is 2 yards long. Marcus puts one patch at each end of the fabric and at each quarter-foot mark. How many patches did Marcus use?

   A 17

   B 18

   C 24

   D 25

2. Kesha feeds her dog, Tiny, 8 ounces of dog food each day. How much dog food, in pounds, does she feed Tiny in 20 days?

   A 6 pounds

   B 8 pounds

   C 10 pounds

   D 12 pounds

3. **Writing to Explain** Artie uses $1\frac{1}{3}$ yards of rope to make the bottom of his hammock stronger. He also uses 10 inches of rope to make each of 4 separate sections of the hammock stronger. How much rope, in yards and in inches, does Artie use in all? Draw a diagram. Explain how the diagram helped solve the problem.

   _____

   _____

   _____

   _____

1. It cost Natalie $32.79 to restring her guitar. If she gives the salesperson a $20 bill and two $10 bills, how much change should she get back?

   A $7.21

   B $7.79

   C $8.21

   D $8.79

2. Renzo bought some gloves that cost $16.42, including tax. He paid for the gloves with four $5 bills and two quarters. How much change should he receive?

   A $3.58

   B $4.08

   C $4.42

   D $4.58

3. **Writing to Explain** The soccer coach bought three new soccer balls. The total cost of the balls was $21.28. The coach used a $20 bill and a $10 bill to pay for the balls. Explain how to count up to find the change. What is a different combination of coins and bills that can be used to make this amount? How did you find the different combination to make the change?

   _____

   _____

   _____

   _____

Name_____

Mrs. Perry had each student in her class cut lengths of string between 5 and 7 inches, and measure them to the nearest $\frac{1}{4}$ inch. She made a line plot of the results.

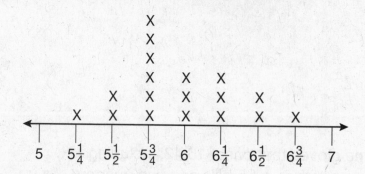

String Lengths (in inches)

1. What is the greatest string length?

   A $5\frac{1}{4}$ in.

   B $5\frac{3}{4}$ in.

   C 6 in.

   D $6\frac{3}{4}$ in.

2. What is the most common string length?

   A 5 in.

   B $5\frac{3}{4}$ in.

   C $6\frac{1}{4}$ in.

   D $6\frac{1}{2}$ in.

3. **Writing to Explain** What is the difference between the longest and the shortest lengths of string in Mrs. Perry's class? Explain.

   _____

   _____

   _____

   _____

1. There are 8 players in a chess tournament. After the tournament each player has to shake hands with every other player. Which number sentence below is the best way to show the number of handshakes?

   A 8×8

   B 7×7

   C $8 + 7 + 6 + 5 + 4 + 3 + 2 + 1$

   D $7 + 6 + 5 + 4 + 3 + 2 + 1$

2. Bella had an apple. She cut it in half, and then she cut it in half again. She ate two pieces of the apple. How many pieces did Bella have left?

   A 1 piece

   B 2 pieces

   C 3 pieces

   D 4 pieces

3. **Writing to Explain** Carlos is setting up tables for a dinner party. He has several square tables. Each can sit 4 guests but he wants to set up the tables so they make one large rectangle. Make a table to show how many tables Carlos will need if he has 16 guests coming to his party.

_____

1. Which term would you use to describe the power line cables shown?

   A perpendicular lines

   B parallel lines

   C intersecting lines

   D plane

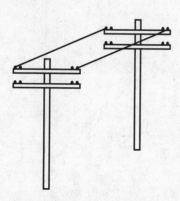

2. Joshua bought a tie for his father. Which term describes the pattern in the tie?

   A perpendicular lines

   B parallel lines

   C intersecting lines

   D plane

3. **Writing to Explain** Debra drew 2 lines, lines *AB* and *CD*. Lines *AB* and *CD* are parallel. She then drew a line *EF* that was perpendicular to line *CD*. If line *EF* intersects line *AB*, is it perpendicular to line *AB*? Draw a picture to help explain your answer.

   _____

   _____

Name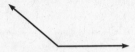_____

1. Jason drew the following angle. Which term describes the angle he drew?

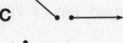

    A right angle

    B acute angle

    C obtuse angle

    D straight angle

2. Lisa drew 2 rays that share an endpoint. Which of the following is Lisa's drawing?

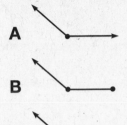

3. Nina's best friend's name starts with a letter that includes 2 parallel lines. Which letter begins her friend's name?

    A A

    B W

    C N

    D X

4. **Writing to Explain** Philip drew a right angle. He then drew a ray between the two rays that formed the right angle. What kind of angle did the new ray form?

_____

1. The angle is $\frac{1}{5}$ of the circle. What is the measure of the angle?

   A 15°

   B 36°

   C 50°

   D 72°

2. Eric cut a pizza into 9 pieces. What is the angle measure of each piece?

   A 20°

   B 30°

   C 40°

   D 90°

3. **Writing to Explain** Find the angle measure of an angle that cuts off $\frac{1}{3}$ of a circle. Use pictures, words, and numbers to show how you found your answer.

_____

_____

_____

_____

1. What is the measure of the angle on the right? Use the beige pattern block to help.

   A 60°

   B 120°

   C 150°

   D 210°

2. How many 30° angles are there in a 210° angle?

   A 5

   B 6

   C 7

   D 8

3. **Writing to Explain** Using pattern blocks, how can you find the measure of the angle below? Use pictures, words, and numbers to show how you found your answer.

   _____

   _____

   _____

   _____

1. Measure the angle shown.

- **A** 30°
- **B** 45°
- **C** 140°
- **D** 180°

2. Measure the angle shown.

- **A** 90°
- **B** 60°
- **C** 45°
- **D** 30°

3. Roberto cuts diagonally across a square park to go home from school. What angle does his path make with the edge of the park?

- **A** 30°
- **B** 45°
- **C** 60°
- **D** 90°

4. Writing to Explain Maya designed two intersecting roads. She drew the roads so that one of the angles at the intersection was 45°. What are the three other angle measures formed by the intersection? Draw a picture and explain your answer.

_____

_____

Name

For **1–3,** use trapezoid *EFGH* at the right.

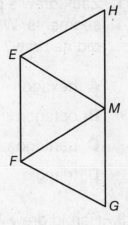

1. The measure of ∠*EFG* is 120°. The measure of ∠*EFM*
   is 60°. Which equation can you use to find the measure
   of ∠*MFG*?

   A $x = 120° - 60°$

   B $120° = x - 60°$

   C $60° = 120° + x$

   D $x = 120° + 60°$

2. Which two angle measures can you add to find the measure
   of ∠*FMH*?

   A ∠*FME* and ∠*MEH*

   B ∠*FME* and ∠*GME*

   C ∠*EMH* and ∠*HME*

   D ∠*FME* and ∠*EMH*

3. **Writing to Explain** The measure of ∠*FMH* is 120°. Explain how
   to find the measure of ∠*FMG* without using a protractor. Use
   words and write an equation to show your answer.

   _____

   _____

   _____

   _____

1. Zack drew a polygon with 8 line segments. What kind of polygon did he draw?

   A hexagon

   B octagon

   C pentagon

   D triangle

2. Allison drew 3 triangles, 5 hexagons, and 4 octagons. How many line segments did she draw?

   A 81

   B 72

   C 71

   D 68

3. Harold drew 21 line segments. Which of the following is a possible number of polygons he drew?

   A 5 quadrilaterals

   B 3 octagons

   C 2 hexagons and 1 octagon

   D 5 triangles and 1 hexagon

4. **Writing to Explain** Marcy has 18 toothpicks. Does she have enough to form 5 quadrilaterals if no quadrilateral shares a toothpick with another quadrilateral?

   _____

   _____

   _____

   _____

1. Norman drew a right triangle. Which triangle did he draw?

A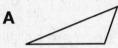

B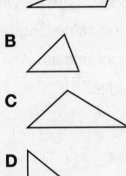

C

D

2. Ursula has 3 line segments that are the same size. What kind of triangle can she make?

A equilateral triangle

B isosceles triangle

C scalene triangle

D right triangle

3. Todd drew an equilateral triangle. Which of the following describes the triangle he drew?

A obtuse

B acute

C scalene

D right

4. Writing to Explain Is it possible to make a triangle with 2 obtuse angles? Draw a picture to help explain your answer.

_____

_____

Name_____

1. Rick drew a rhombus. What other term could you use to describe what Rick drew based on what you know about quadrilaterals?

   A parallelogram

   B pentagon

   C trapezoid

   D hexagon

2. Sally drew a quadrilateral. Which of the following must be true about what Sally drew?

   A The opposite sides are parallel.

   B Each side is the same length.

   C There are 4 right angles.

   D There are 4 sides.

3. Lacey drew a trapezoid. Which of the following must be true about what Lacey drew?

   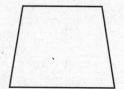

   A There is at least 1 right angle.

   B One pair of sides is parallel.

   C There are no right angles.

   D Three of the sides are the same length.

4. **Writing to Explain** Describe why a square is also a rhombus, a rectangle, a parallelogram, and a quadrilateral.

   _____

   _____

   _____

   _____

1. Which line is a line of symmetry?

A

B

C

D

2. Which letter has more than one line of symmetry?

A **B**

B **H**

C **F**

D **K**

3. Writing to Explain How many lines of symmetry does the figure below have? Draw each one. Explain how reflections can be used to check that a line is a line of symmetry.

_____

_____

Name_____

1. Which generalizations can you make about these polygons?

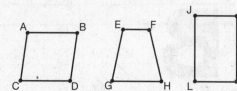

A Each shape is a quadrilateral with sides of the same length.

B Each shape is a quadrilateral with at least 1 pair of opposite sides that are parallel.

C Each shape is a quadrilateral with 4 right angles.

D All quadrilaterals are parallelograms.

2. Which generalizations can you make about these triangles?

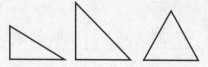

A All triangles have 1 right angle.

B All triangles have 3 angles and 3 sides.

C All sides of a triangle are equal in length.

D All the angles of a triangle are equal.

3. Writing to Explain Draw a right triangle and an equilateral triangle. Describe how the angles in each are similar and different.

_____

_____

_____

_____

Name_____

1. Which has the same value as 4 × 6? (1-1)

A 4 + 4 + 4 + 4

B 6 + 4 + 6 + 4

C 6 + 6 + 6 + 6

D 4 + 6

2. Juan bought 3 bags of oranges. Each bag had 1 orange in it. How many oranges did he buy? (1-3)

A 0

B 1

C 2

D 3

3. Which is a way to find 6 × 9? (1-4)

A 12 + 96

B 34 + 24

C 24 + 30

D 36 + 15

4. Katie handed out seat tickets for the school play. Below are the first five seat numbers she gave out. If the pattern continues, what are the next three numbers she will give out? (1-5)

16, 24, 32, 40, 48, ☐, ☐, ☐

A 54, 66, 72

B 56, 60, 64

C 56, 64, 72

D 58, 66, 72

5. An astronaut collected 56 moon rocks. She has 7 bags. Which number sentence shows how many moon rocks she can put in each bag if she puts the same number in each bag? (1-6)

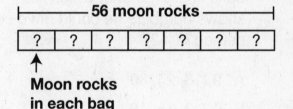

Moon rocks in each bag

A 56 − 7 = 49

B 56 ÷ 7 = 8

C 56 + 7 = 63

D 56 × 7 = 392

Name_____

6. What is 42 ÷ 7? (1-9)

   A 7

   B 6

   C 5

   D 4

7. Each package has 9 ping-pong balls.

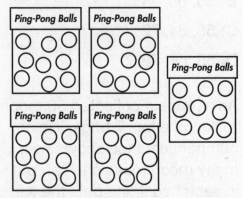

If Ricardo counted the ping-pong balls in groups of 9, which list shows numbers he could have named? (1-2)

   A 9, 18, 24, 30

   B 9, 12, 15, 18

   C 9, 18, 27, 36

   D 18, 24, 30, 36

8. What is the quotient of 0 ÷ 3? (1-8)

_____

9. It takes Carlos 5 minutes to bike one mile. How many minutes would it take him to bike 4 miles? (1-2)

_____

10. Pablo has 6 balloons. His sister has 3 times as many balloons. What number sentence can be used to find the number of balloons Pablo's sister has? (1-10)

? balloons in all			
Pablo's sister	6	6	6

3 times as many

Pablo   6

_____

11. What number makes the number sentence true? (1-3)

$5 \times 3 = \boxed{} \times 5$

_____

12. What multiplication expression can be broken apart into $(3 \times 4) + (3 \times 4)$ using the distributive property? (1-4)

_____

13. What number makes both number sentences true? (1-7)

$8 \times \boxed{} = 48$
$48 \div 8 = \boxed{}$

_____

14. What multiplication sentences are in the same fact family as $54 \div 6 = \boxed{}$ (1-9)

_____

15. Henry's dresser is 7 times as long as the length of a piece of paper. The length of the piece of paper is 6 inches. What is the length of the dresser? Draw a picture and write an equation to solve. (1-10)

_____

_____

16. What are the next three numbers in the pattern? (1-5)

23, 29, 35, 41, 47

_____

17. Write a multiplication sentence for $3 + 3 + 3 + 3 + 3 = 15$. (1-1)

_____

18. What multiplication fact can help you find $4 \div 4$? (1-8)

_____

19. Mr. Sanchez has 25 screwdrivers. He puts them in 5 equal rows. How many screwdrivers are in each row? Draw a picture to help divide. (1-6)

_____

20. Neil has a collection of 40 shells that he wants to arrange in 5 equal groups. Write a fact family that shows how Neil could arrange his shells. (1-7)

_____

_____

Name_____

Mark the best answer.

1. Mail boxes are lined up on Maple Street in the pattern shown below. (2-2)

What number belongs on the blank mail box?

A 12

B 13

C 15

D 17

2. Georgia writes a number pattern on the chalkboard. What are the next three numbers in this pattern? (2-1)

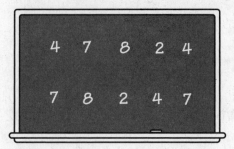

A 2, 4, 7

B 4, 7, 8

C 7, 8, 2

D 8, 2, 4

3. What rule can be used to find the number of wheels on 7 tricycles? (2-4)

Number of Tricycles	3	5	7	9
Number of Wheels	9	15	■	27

A Add 6   **C** Multiply by 3

B Subtract 2   **D** Divide by 3

4. Lauren is making a design with tiles, which are shaped like squares. She cuts yarn to go around each square. How many inches of yarn does she need for a square with sides that are 6 inches long? (2-5)

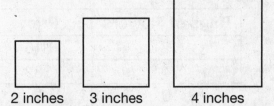

2 inches   3 inches   4 inches

Inches on One Side	2	3	4	6
Inches of Yarn	8	12	16	?

A 20   **C** 24

B 22   **D** 28

Name_____

5. Mr. Marvin needs to put equal groups of people at tables in the cafeteria. The chart shows the number of tables for different numbers of people.

Number of Persons	24	36	42	54
Number of Tables	4	6	■	9

What rule can be used to find how many tables are needed if there are 42 persons? (2-4)

A Divide by 6

B Divide by 8

C Add 12

D Multiply by 6

6. Glen buys silk flowers in bags to make bouquets for a party. The chart shows the prices of different numbers of bags of flowers.

Bags of Flowers	Price
2	$16
4	$32
6	■
8	$64

What is the price of 6 bags of flowers? (2-3)

_____

7. Roberto has 20 crayons. Twelve crayons are red. The rest are blue or yellow. He has 2 more blue crayons than yellow. How many yellow crayons does he have? (2-6)

_____

8. Jordy writes this pattern in his notebook.

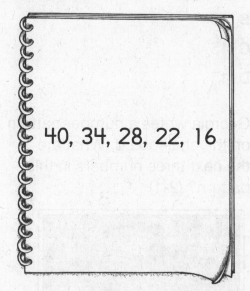

40, 34, 28, 22, 16

What is a rule for the pattern? (2-2)

_____

9. Carly writes this number pattern in chalk on the sidewalk. (2-1)

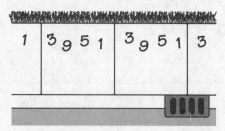

1 3 9 5 1 3 9 5 1 3

Write the next three numbers in the pattern.

_____

Name_____

10. Lockers in the Green Street School are lined up in the pattern shown below.

Write the number that belongs on the blank locker. (2-2)

_____

11. Jian is measuring the sides of triangles. If the pattern continues, how many inches will he measure all around if one side is 6 inches long? (2-5)

3 inches   4 inches   5 inches

Inches (One Side)	3	4	5	6
Inches (All Sides)	9	12	15	■

_____

12. There are 28 envelopes on a desk. Twenty envelopes are white and the rest are tan or blue. There are four more tan envelopes than blue envelopes. How many envelopes are blue? (2-6)

_____

13. Mr. Chen buys boxes of crayons for his students. The chart shows the different prices for the boxes of crayons.

Total Number of Boxes	Total Price
2	$8
4	$16
6	■
10	$40

What is the total price for 6 boxes of crayons? (2-3)

_____

1. Which is less than 107,084? (3-3)

   A 107,048

   B 107,089

   C 107,408

   D 107,804

2. A country covers about 467,200 square miles. Which number is less than 467,200? (3-3)

   A 476,200

   B 467,200

   C 466,200

   D 470,600

3. A baseball stadium had 32,508 visitors on Monday, 32,580 visitors on Tuesday, and 32,480 visitors on Wednesday. Which lists these numbers from least to greatest? (3-4)

   A 32,580   32,508   32,480

   B 32,480   32,508   32,580

   C 32,508   32,580   32,480

   D 32,480   32,580   32,508

4. Bobby has 230 marbles to put in jars. He wants the jars to hold either 100 marbles or 10 marbles. Which is a way he can arrange the marbles? (3-6)

   A 23 hundreds

   B 2 hundreds 30 tens

   C 1 hundred 3 tens

   D 2 hundreds 3 tens

5. The table shows the areas of four lakes. Which of the four lakes has the greatest area? (3-4)

Lakes	Surface Area (Square miles)
Lake Huron	23,000
Lake Michigan	22,000
Lake Superior	32,000
Lake Erie	10,000

   A Lake Huron

   B Lake Michigan

   C Lake Superior

   D Lake Erie

6. The place-value blocks show the number of cereal boxes that are on the store shelves. How many boxes are there? (3-1)

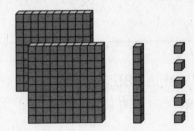

   A 115

   B 151

   C 215

   D 251

Name_____

7. Which number will have the same result, when rounded to the nearest hundred or thousand? (3-5)

   A 1,049

   B 1,118 and 5

   C 1,179

   D 2,149

8. What is the standard form of 3,000 + 700 + 9? (3-1)

_____

9. Sonia has three bracelets. She wears them all at the same time but in a different order each day. How many different bracelet combinations does Sonia have to choose from? (3-6)

_____

10. What is 285,624 rounded to the nearest ten thousand? (3-5)

_____

11. A jar of coins contains 6,245 pennies. What is 6,245 rounded to the nearest hundred? (3-5)

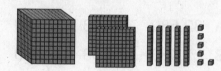

6,200   6,245   6,300

_____

12. In the number 436,621, which places contain digits where one digit is ten times as great as the other? (3-2)

_____

_____

_____

13. Write the number shown by the place-value blocks in word form. (3-1)

_____

_____

_____

14. The number 199,557 contains two sets of digits in which one digit is ten times as great as the other. What are the values of the digits in each set? (3-2)

_____

_____

_____

15. The table shows the number of tickets sold for each movie. How would you write the movies in order from the least amount of tickets sold to the greatest amount sold? (3-4)

Movie	Number of Tickets Sold
The Adventures of Pete the Penguin	915,432
Into the Wilderness	877,642
Robots, Robots, Robots	951,387

_____

_____

_____

16. Tammy wants to get change for $1. The only coins she can get are half dollars, quarters, and nickels. How many different ways can she get $1 using only these coins? (3-6)

_____

17. What are the values of the 7s in the number 17,372? (3-2)

_____

_____

18. Jess is thinking of a 4-digit number. Roger is thinking of a 3-digit number. Whose number is greater? How do you know? (3-3)

_____

_____

_____

_____

_____

_____

19. Three new apartments went up for rent this week. The rents for the apartments were $1,550, $1,475, and $1,499. Write the rents in order from greatest to least. (3-4)

_____

_____

Name_____

Mark the best answer.

1. Amanda's ant farm holds 56,732 ants. Jim's ant farm holds 48,841 ants. How many more ants does Amanda's ant farm hold? (4-4)

   A 17,891

   B 7,981

   C 7,891

   D 2,191

2. The following table shows cans collected for a food drive.

   Cans Collected

January	419
February	385
March	452

   Which is the best estimate of the total number of cans collected? (4-2)

   A 1,300

   B 1,100

   C 800

   D 700

3. Ernest went to a clothing store with $200 and bought a winter coat for $129 including the tax. How much money did Ernest have left after his purchase? (4-5)

   A $51

   B $71

   C $91

   D $171

4. Daisy's class wants to collect 273 toys for homeless children. So far, they have gathered 183. Which picture models the number of toys they need? (4-6)

   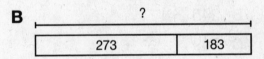

Name_____

5. There are 3,164 students at North Elementary School. There are 2,918 students at South Elementary School. How many students are there at both elementary schools (4-3)

   A 6,172

   B 6,082

   C 6,072

   D 5,082

6. Julie folded 112 paper cranes and 247 paper dogs. To find $112 + 247$, Julie made a multiple of ten, as shown below. What is the missing number? (4-1)
   $112 + 247 = 110 + \boxed{} = 359$

   A 137

   B 245

   C 249

   D 259

7. The auditorium has 3,000 chairs set up for a band performance. There are 1,585 tickets sold so far. How many seats are left? (4-5)

   _____

8. Last year, 2,828 people saw the school play. This year, 3,568 people saw the play. How many people saw the play last year and this year combined? (4-3)

   _____

9. What number makes the number sentence true? (4-1)
   $92 + 87 = \boxed{} + 92$

   _____

10. Marissa has 4,582 beads to use to make a border on a quilt. She has already used 2,349 beads. How many beads does she have left to use? (4-4)

    _____

11. The following table shows the amount of money raised for a fundraiser.

Money Raised	
Spring	$478
Summer	$629
Fall	$389

    Write a number sentence that uses rounding to the hundreds place to estimate the total amount of money raised? (4-2)

    _____

12. April has 512 balloons. She has 236 blue balloons, 148 green balloons, and the rest are red balloons. Use the diagram below to find the number of red balloons. (4-6)

    512 balloons

236	148	?

    _____

13. Find 8,000 − 5,436. (4-5)

_____

14. Bea collected bottle caps and Dani collected tabs from aluminum cans. How many more bottle caps did Bea have than Dani had can tabs? (4-4)

Collections	
Bea's bottle caps	113
Dani's can tabs	96

_____

15. Dale drove from Chicago to Milwaukee, and then to Minneapolis. The total distance he traveled was 430 miles. The distance from Chicago to Milwaukee is 93 miles. How many miles, *m*, did Dale travel from Milwaukee to Minneapolis? (4-6)

430 miles

93	*m*

_____

16. The average home attendance at a team's basketball games last year was 13,796. In a larger city, the average number was 21,776. Round to the nearest thousand. About how many more people attended games in the larger city? (4-2)

_____

_____

17. Maya, Paloma, and Natalia each earned a quarter for every pair of socks they matched from the laundry. If Maya matched 12 pairs of socks, Paloma matched 15, and Natalia matched 8, how many quarters did they earn in all? Explain how you can use mental math to find the answer. (4-1)

_____

_____

Name_____

Mark the best answer.

1. The art teacher has 6 packages of poster board. There are 30 pieces of poster board in each package. How many pieces of poster board does the art teacher have? (5-2)

   A 36

   B 150

   C 180

   D 306

2. There are 36 inches in one yard. Nadia has 8 yards of ribbon. Use rounding to estimate how many inches of ribbon Nadia has. (5-5)

   A 400 inches

   B 320 inches

   C 260 inches

   D 240 inches

3. Which shows one way to use breaking apart to find 6×47? (5-3)

   A $(1 \times 47) - (1 \times 6)$

   B $(6 \times 4) + (6 \times 7)$

   C $(6 \times 40) - (1 \times 7)$

   D $(6 \times 40) + (6 \times 7)$

4. Alex's home is 394 miles from Columbus, Ohio. If Alex makes 5 one-way trips from his home to Columbus, how many miles will he travel? (5-4)

   A 3,945 miles

   B 2,030 miles

   C 2,000 miles

   D 1,970 miles

5. Which shows another way to find $10 + 10 + 10 + 10 + 10 + 10 + 10$? (5-1)

   A 7×1

   B 7×10

   C 7×100

   D $7 \times 1,000$

6. Mr. Grasso drove 54 miles an hour for 3 hours. He used compensation to find how far he drove. First, he multiplied $50 \times 3 = 150$. What should Mr. Grasso do next? (5-4)

   A $150 + 50 = 200$

   B $150 + 12 = 162$

   C $150 - 12 = 138$

   D $150 - 54 = 96$

7. Ms. Bennett is making brownies for a school bake sale. She wants 8 platters of brownies with 22 brownies on each platter. Which is a reasonable estimate for the number of brownies that Ms. Bennett makes? (5-6)

   A 100, because 8×22 is about $5 \times 20 = 100$

   B 160, because 8×22 is about $8 \times 20 = 160$

   C 240, because 8×22 is about $8 \times 30 = 240$

   D 300, because 8×22 is about $10 \times 30 = 300$

8. Betty Jo practices the piano about 28 minutes each day. Use rounding to estimate the amount of time Betty Jo practices the piano in 7 days. Write a number sentence to show your work. (5-5)

_____

_____

9. Write a number sentence that shows another way to find $100 + 100 + 100 + 100 + 100 + 100$. (5-1)

_____

10. The tickets for all 3 performances of the school play have been sold. There are 189 seats in the school auditorium. Write a number sentence that uses rounding to estimate the total number of tickets that have been sold. (5-5)

_____

_____

11. Write an expression that uses breaking apart to find 7×28. (5-3)

_____

Name_____

12. The florist is making centerpieces for some tables. She puts 16 roses into each of 9 vases. How many roses did the florist use? (5-4)

_____

13. Use breaking apart to find the product for 9×36. (5-3)

$(9 \times$ ____$) + (9 \times$ ___$)$

____ + ____ = ____

14. Each section of a ballpark has the same number of seats. There are about 200 seats in each section. About how many seats are in 4 sections? (5-2)

_____

15. Draw a picture to show which number is greater: 7×100 or 7×10. (5-1)

_____

16. Use basic facts to find the product. (5-2)

$30 \times 8 =$

_____

17. Martin wants to buy 5 games that cost $23 each. He uses the place-value blocks below to help him multiply. How much will all 5 games cost? (5-3)

_____

18. Shelly saves $8 each week. Use rounding to estimate the amount she will have saved after 32 weeks. Write a number sentence to show your work. (5-5)

_____

19. Maria knows there are 24 hours in one day and 7 days in one week. So, she figured out that there are 168 hours in one week. Is her answer reasonable? Explain why or why not. (5-6)

_____

_____

_____

_____

1. Part of the calculation for 7×38 is shown below. Which is the missing partial product? (6-1)

   A 64
   B 56
   C 38
   D 21

   $$
   \begin{array}{r}
   38 \\
   \times\ 7 \\
   \hline
   \square\square \\
   +\ 210 \\
   \hline
   266
   \end{array}
   $$

2. There are 134 musicians in a marching band. Each musician has 8 buttons on his or her uniform. How many buttons are there in all? (6-4)

   A 942
   B 1,052
   C 1,072
   D 1,282

3. Richard bought four Dogwood shrubs. Each Dogwood shrub costs $18. How much did Richard spend? (6-2)

   ? dollars

   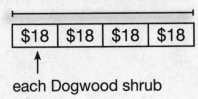

   each Dogwood shrub

   A $36
   B $48
   C $60
   D $72

4. Four medical colleges each have a class of 86 new students. How many new students start medical school at the same time? (6-2)

   A 324
   B 330
   C 344
   D 362

5. There were 26 women registered for a water-skiing contest. Twice as many men as women competed. Which shows the number of men in the water-skiing contest? (6-3)

   A 26
   B 39
   C 52
   D 56

6. Sara can make 25 gift tags using 1 package of labels. If she uses 5 packages of labels, how many gift tags can she make? (6-1)

   A 50
   B 125
   C 300
   D 1,025

Name _____

7. A train has an engine pulling 7 coach cars. Each coach car can seat 44 passengers. If all the coaches are full, how many passengers are on the train? (6-2)

   A 288

   B 291

   C 298

   D 308

8. Karla sells kayaks. Her best 2-person ocean kayak was on sale for $1,119. Last week, Karla sold 5 of those kayaks. What is the total amount Karla collected from the sales? (6-5)

   _____

9. Some History Club students took a bus trip. Each student paid $27 for the bus ticket. They visited a museum and a fort. Admission to the museum was $5 for students and $8 for adults. All tickets to tour the fort were free. What information is NOT needed to find how much each student spent on the trip? (6-6)

   _____

   _____

10. Ms. Burke makes 3 round trips each month. The total distance of each trip is 5,944 kilometers. What is the total distance of her trips each month? (6-4)

    _____

11. David bought a 3-ring binder for $4, a package of pencils for $1, and two packages of paper. What information is needed to find the total amount David spent before tax? (6-6)

    _____

    _____

12. An employee gets paid $1,035 each week. How much money will the employee get paid for working 6 weeks? How can you use estimation to check the reasonableness of your answer? (6-5)

    _____

    _____

    _____

13. An elementary school has 6 fourth-grade classes. Each class has 29 students. How many students are in the fourth grade? (6-3)

    _____

Name_____

14. Channel WMAT played a music video 49 times a day for 3 days. What partial products would you use to find how many times the music video was played in all? (6-1)

_____

15. The total cost to install a new swimming pool is $2,725. This includes materials, labor, tax, and delivery. If 3 orders to install the same kind of pool were taken on Monday, what would the total be in dollars? (6-5)

_____

16. A fast food restaurant uses 350 pounds of fries each month. How many pounds of french fries are used in 4 months? (6-4)

_____

17. Eli spends about $58 each week filling up his car with gas. How much does Eli spend on gas in 4 weeks? Explain each step you took to find your answer. (6-3)

_____

_____

_____

_____

18. Ms. Green drove 7 miles from her house to Franklin. Franklin is 6 miles east of Clinton. From Franklin, she drove 5 miles to Burlington. Then she drove 18 miles from Burlington to Milton. How far did Ms. Green drive in all, from her house to Milton? Identify the extra or missing information. Solve if possible. (6-6)

_____

_____

_____

_____

Mark the best answer.

1. There are 14 rows of windmills with 38 windmills in each row. Which shows the best way to estimate how many windmills there are all together? (7-3)

A 10×30

B 20×30

C 10×40

D 20×40

2. Madge is making 20 bracelets to sell at the fair. She needs 17 beads for each bracelet. How many beads does she need in all? (7-1)

A 340

B 200

C 140

D 34

3. Dana bought 12 bags of shells when she was on vacation at the beach. There are 54 shells in each bag. Which shows the best estimate of how many shells Dana bought? (7-4)

A 100

B 500

C 1,000

D 1,500

4. There are 24 students in Mr. Kane's class. Each student needs 12 sheets of paper for an art project. Which shows the best way to use compatible numbers to estimate how many sheets of paper Mr. Kane needs? (7-4)

A 30×20

B 30×10

C 25×10

D 20×20

5. Diego bought 30 books of postage stamps. There are 20 stamps in each book. How many stamps did Diego buy? (7-2)

A 60

B 600

C 6,000

D 60,000

6. There are 30 rows of cars in a parking lot. If 14 cars can fit in each row, how many cars can be parked in the parking lot? (7-1)

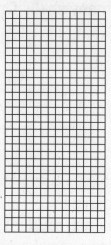

A 420

B 300

C 120

D 42

7. Mr. Tyler bought 2 sandwiches that cost $5 each. He also bought 3 salads that cost $4 each. He gave the clerk a $50 bill. How much change should he get back? (7-5)

_____

8. Fred is painting the boards on his backyard fence. There are 20 boards in each section of fence. If there are 20 sections, how many boards does Fred have to paint? (7-2)

_____

9. Write a number sentence that shows the best way to use rounding to estimate 82 × 47. (7-3)

_____

10. Rita buys 22 cases of water for the school picnic. There are 24 bottles of water in a case. Using compatible numbers, write a number sentence that shows about how many bottles of water Rita bought. (7-4)

_____

11. Complete the number sentence. (7-2)

50 × 40 = _____

12. Colin put 3 rows of pictures on a bulletin board. He placed 6 pictures in each row. Jessie put 4 rows of pictures on a different bulletin board. She placed 5 pictures in each row. How many more pictures did Jessie put on her bulletin board? (7-5)

_____

Name_____

13. The owner of a party store ordered 30 boxes of American flags. There are 30 flags in each box. How many flags did the owner of the store order? (7-2)

_____

14. The tree in Chuck's yard is 48 feet tall. About how many inches tall is the tree? (7-3)

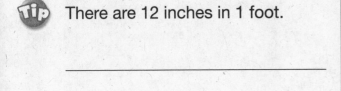 There are 12 inches in 1 foot.

_____

_____

15. Marie is making 16 packages of greeting cards. She places 10 cards in each pack. How many greeting cards does she need to make all the packages? (7-1)

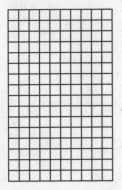

_____

16. The school library places paperback books in a section with 21 shelves. Each shelf fits 38 books. Use compatible numbers to estimate the number of books that the library can fit on the shelves. (7-4)

_____

17. Together Paul and Jack earned $72 washing cars. Jack washed twice as many cars as Paul. If Paul washed 3 cars, how much did they charge to wash each car? Explain how you know. (7-5)

_____

_____

_____

_____

_____

_____

Mark the best answer.

1. Brian has filled 36 pages in his stamp collector's album. Each page has 25 stamps. Brian is using the table below to figure out how many stamps he has in all. Which number is missing from the table? (8-1)

	20	5
30	□	150
6	120	30

   A 600

   B 500

   C 60

   D 50

2. What is 40 × 58? (8-4)

   A 232

   B 2,320

   C 3,220

   D 20,320

3. Which shows one correct way to use partial products to find 70 × 96? (8-3)

   A (70 × 70) + (30 × 8)

   B (70 × 90) + (70 × 6)

   C (60 × 90) + (10 × 6)

   D (50 × 48) + (20 × 48)

4. Kat runs 12 miles each week. How many miles will she have run after 20 weeks? (8-3)

   A 32 miles

   B 200 miles

   C 240 miles

   D 400 miles

5. Diego drives a shuttle van at a theme park. Each day, he makes 36 trips from the parking lot to the visitor center. His van can hold 18 passengers. Diego used partial products to find the total number of riders he can carry each day. What is the missing partial product? (8-2)

$$\begin{array}{r} 18 \\ \times\ 36 \\ \hline 48 \\ 60 \\ \boxed{} \\ +\ 300 \\ \hline \end{array}$$

   A 11

   B 24

   C 210

   D 240

Name_____

6. Use the grid to help you find 12 × 33. (8-1)

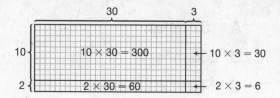

   A 394

   B 396

   C 496

   D 500

7. Mr. Berk bought 14 new globes that his students could use to learn about Earth. Each globe cost $76. How much did the new globes cost in all? (8-4)

   A $380

   B $954

   C $1,060

   D $1,064

8. Record the partial products for 37 × 42. Then add to find the product. (8-2)

$$\begin{array}{r} 42 \\ \times\ 37 \\ \hline \end{array}$$

9. The video store ordered 40 boxes of a new film called *Mad About Manatees.* There were 12 copies in each box. How many DVDs in all did the video store order of *Mad About Manatees?* (8-3)

_____

10. Look at the table shown below. What multiplication problem does it represent? (8-1)

	30	5
60		
1		

11. The manatee is a gentle sea mammal that eats sea plants. Suppose a medium-size adult manatee eats 98 pounds of plants in one day. How many pounds of plants would this size manatee eat in 2 weeks? (8-5)

_____

Name_____

12. A museum features exhibits on the art, history, and way of life of an ancient people. During a show, one room held 11 glass display cases. Each case held 32 different hand-crafted objects. How many objects would you have seen in that room? (8-4)

_____

13. Multiply to find all the partial products for 68 × 42. Record the partial products in the boxes. Then add to find the product. (8-2)

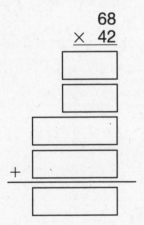

$$\begin{array}{r} 68 \\ \times\ 42 \\ \end{array}$$

14. At Madison Elementary school, no teacher has more than 24 students at a time. If there are 30 teachers at the school, how many students could there be? (8-3)

_____

15. Problem 1: Author Annelle Rigsby writes historical novels for young readers. Her first book, *Race to Kitty Hawk*, has 84 pages. Her third book, *Kidnapped in Key West*, has 136 pages. How many pages shorter is Annelle Rigsby's first book than her third book?

_____

Problem 2: How many more pages are in 15 copies of *Kidnapped in Key West* than in *Race to Kitty Hawk*? Explain how you found your answer. (8-5)

_____
_____
_____
_____
_____
_____
_____
_____
_____

Name_____

Mark the best answer.

1. There are 4,800 children who go to school in Grades 1–8 in the town of Warren. How many children are in each grade if the number in each is equal? (9-1)

   A 60

   B 600

   C 6,000

   D 60,000

2. What is the quotient? (9-4)

   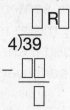

   A 3 R9

   B 8 R3

   C 8 R7

   D 9 R3

3. The play is performed 7 times. A total of 1,585 tickets were sold and the same number of people attended each performance. About how many people attended each performance? (9-3)

   A 300

   B 200

   C 150

   D 100

4. What is 95 ÷ 6? (9-4)

   A 10 R1

   B 15 R1

   C 15 R5

   D 16 R5

5. Deanna has 43 ceramic tiles to make a decorative pattern on her kitchen floor. She will use the same number of tiles in each corner of the floor. She will use any remaining tiles to make a design in the middle. How many tiles can she use in each corner, and how many tiles will she have left for the middle? (9-5)

   A Each corner will have 11 tiles. There will be 3 left over.

   B Each corner will have 10 tiles. There will be 3 left over.

   C Each corner will have 9 tiles There will be 14 left over.

   D Each corner will have 9 tiles. There will be 0 left over.

Name_____

6. Miguel spent $207 on 7 model airplane kits. Which number sentence shows the best way to estimate the amount he spent for each kit? (9-2)

A $140 ÷ 7 = $20

B $210 ÷ 7 = $30

C 7 × $200 = $1,400

D 7 × $210 = $1,470

7. Mrs. Lincoln steamed 32 clams for a family picnic. There were 5 people eating clams and each person ate an equal number of clams. How many clams were left over? (9-5)

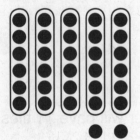

A 6 left

B 5 left

C 2 left

D 1 left

8. A jeweler made 96 necklaces. She put an equal number of necklaces in each of 5 display trays. How many necklaces are in each tray? How many remaining necklaces are not displayed? (9-4)

_____

_____

9. An astronaut collected 56 moon rocks. She has 7 bags to put them in. Write a number sentence that shows how many moon rocks she can put in each bag if she puts the same number in each bag. (9-6)

56 moon rocks

?	?	?	?	?	?	?

↑ moon rocks in each bag

_____

10. A case of toothpicks has 5,400 toothpicks. There are 9 boxes of toothpicks in the case. How many toothpicks are in each box? (9-1)

_____

11. Estimate the quotient for 627 ÷ 9. Explain how you found your answer. (9-2)

_____

_____

_____

Name_____

12. Writing to Explain Tyler has 83 football cards that he wants to put into an album. Each page holds 6 cards. How many pages will he need? How many spaces will he have left for new cards? Explain your answer. (9-5)

_____

_____

_____

_____

13. Nick uses 8 dowels to make one birdhouse. If he bought 1,581 dowels, about how many birdhouses will he be able to make? Explain. (9-3)

_____

_____

_____

14. What number sentence comes next in the pattern? (9-1)

$21 \div 7 = 3$

$210 \div 7 = 30$

$2,100 \div 7 = 300$

_____

15. There are 18 people waiting for a ride. A car holds 4 people. How many cars are needed? (9-4)

_____

16. A box has 640 nails. Each model boat needs 8 nails to hold it together. How many model boats can be made? (9-1)

_____

17. Casey is saving to buy a new computer that costs $2,450. She saves an equal amount of money each month for 5 months. About how much does she need to save each month to buy the computer? (9-3)

_____

18. Aramis has 36 coins that he wants to display on 3 pages in his coin album. Write a number sentence that shows how many coins he can put on each page. (9-6)

Aramis's 36 coins

?	?	?

↑
Coins on each page

_____

Name_____

Mark the best answer.

1. Gus picked 16 sunflowers to give equally to his 2 sisters. He uses repeated subtraction to find how many sunflowers each sister should get. How many times will he subtract 2 until the answer is zero? (10-1)

   A 2

   B 8

   C 14

   D 16

2. For the division problem 367 ÷ 5, in what place will you start dividing? (10-6)

   A ones

   B tens

   C hundreds

   D thousands

3. The school musical was performed 5 times. A total of 875 people attended the shows. The same number of people went to each performance. How many people attended each show? (10-5)

   A 190

   B 175

   C 160

   D 150

4. Jo collects coins. She has 23 Euro coins, 19 British coins, 4 Hungarian coins, and 2 Polish coins. She displays them all equally in 3 glass cupboards. Which shows how she found the number of coins to put in each cupboard? (10-8)

   A 3 × 48

   B 48 ÷ 3

   C 23 × 3

   D 19 ÷ 3

5. Daisy has 93 planks of wood to make a fence surrounding her house. She will use the same number of planks for each side of the fence. How many planks of wood will she use for each of the four sides of the fence? (10-3)

   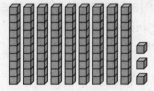

   A Each side will use 20 planks of wood. There will be 3 left over.

   B Each side will use 23 planks of wood. There will be 1 left over.

   C Each side will use 10 planks of wood. There will be 14 left over.

   D Each side will use 24 planks of wood. There will be 0 left over.

Name_____

6. What is 411 ÷ 6? (10-5)

    A 36 R2

    B 41 R1

    C 68 R3

    D 71 R1

7. An amateur rocket club spent $1,313 on 7 rocket kits. Which number sentence shows the best way to estimate the amount the club spent for each kit? (10-7)

    A $1,000 ÷ 10 = $100

    B $1,400 ÷ 7 = $200

    C 7 × $1,200 = $8,400

    D 7 × $1,300 = $9,100

8. Tyrese's school is holding a basketball tournament. A total of 65 students are playing in the tournament. How many teams of 5 can play in the tournament? (10-2)

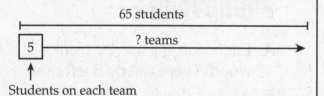

65 students

? teams

5

↑

Students on each team

_____

9. A jeweler made 96 necklaces. She put an equal number of necklaces in each of 4 display trays. How many necklaces are in each tray? (10-4)

_____

10. Rachel collected 56 rocks at the beach. She is placing them into bags to give to her friends. She says that if she puts 4 rocks in each bag, she will have 16 rocks left after she makes 10 bags. Is she correct? Explain. (10-2)

_____

_____

11. Dennis had 26 slices of bread to make sandwiches. If each sandwich has 2 slices of bread, how many sandwiches can Dennis make? (10-1)

_____

12. Nick uses 3 dowels to make one birdhouse. If he bought 85 dowels, how many birdhouses will he be able to make and how many will be left over? (10-3)

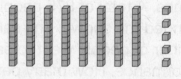

_____

_____

Name_____

13. Each locker requires 3 feet of space. How many lockers can the school build with 43 feet of space? How much space will the school have left? (10-4)

_____

_____

_____

14. Can you tell the number of digits that will be in the quotient for 627 ÷ 9 by only looking at the problem? Explain. (10-6)

_____

_____

_____

_____

15. A school spent $1,902 on 6 new microscopes for science classes. Each microscope costs the same amount of money. Find the cost of 1 microscope. Show all of your work. (10-7)

_____

_____

_____

_____

_____

16. Tara does work for her neighbors. When she does work outdoors she earns $13 an hour. When she works indoors she earns $7 an hour. Last month she did 24 hours of work outdoors and 11 hours of work indoors. How much did Tara earn last month? (10-8)

_____

17. Marcus has 618 trading cards. He wants to put an equal number into each of 5 books to display them. How many cards will there be in each book? How many will be left over? (10-5)

_____

_____

18. A plane flying from Seattle to Washington, D.C. travels 2,310 miles in 6 hours. If the plane travels the same speed, how many miles does the plane travel each hour? (10-7)

_____

Name_____

Mark the best answer.

1. Which statement is true? (11-2)

   A The only factors of 7 are 7 and 1.

   B The only factors of 8 are 8 and 1.

   C The only factors of 9 are 9 and 1.

   D The only factors of 14 are 14 and 1.

2. What are four multiples of 7? (11-3)

   A 1, 2, 3, 7

   B 7, 14, 21, 28

   C 14, 21, 27, 35

   D 7, 17, 70, 77

3. What are two fractions that represent point *M*? (11-5)

   A $\frac{2}{8}$ and $\frac{1}{4}$

   B $\frac{4}{8}$ and $\frac{1}{2}$

   C $\frac{2}{10}$ and $\frac{1}{5}$

   D $\frac{2}{8}$ and $\frac{4}{10}$

4. Which lists all of the factors of 49? (11-1)

   A 1, 49

   B 1, 7, 49

   C 1, 24, 49

   D 1, 49, 98

5. Luis and Bill raced from their house to the big tree in the backyard, but stopped when their mother called them in. They decided that whoever had gotten farther would win the race. Luis made it $\frac{5}{8}$ of the way and Bill made it $\frac{3}{8}$ of the way to the tree. Which symbol makes the comparison true? (11-6)

   $\frac{5}{8}$ ◯ $\frac{3}{8}$

   A <

   B ×

   C =

   D >

Name_____

6. Which statement would **NOT** be used in an explanation of how the drawing shows that $\frac{4}{12} = \frac{1}{3}$? (11-8)

A 1 of the 3 rectangles are filled with shaded circles.

B In the rectangles, 4 out of the 12 circles are shaded.

C Both $\frac{4}{12}$ and $\frac{1}{3}$ describe the part that is shaded.

D 3 out of the 3 rectangles are shaded.

7. What number should go in the box to make the fractions equivalent? (11-4)

$$\frac{6}{10} = \frac{3}{\square}$$

_____

8. Write all the factors of 15. (11-1)

_____

9. Which of the following numbers is prime? (11-2)

48   21   11   32

_____

10. The table shows the different types of juice Pete drank yesterday.

Type of Juice	Cup
Orange	$\frac{2}{3}$
Apple	$\frac{5}{6}$
Berry	$\frac{1}{12}$

Write the fractions in order from least to greatest. (11-7)

_____

11. Which of the following numbers is a multiple of 7? (11-3)

12, 15, 32, 35

_____

12. What is the missing number that makes the fractions equivalent? (11-4)

$$\frac{3}{4} = \frac{9}{\square}$$

_____

Name_____

13. Which point represents an equivalent fraction for $\frac{3}{5}$? (11-5)

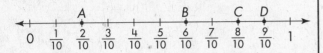

_____

14. Write the fractions listed below in order from greatest to least. (11-7)

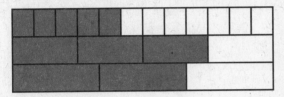

$\frac{5}{12}$, $\frac{3}{4}$, $\frac{2}{3}$

_____

15. Karen measured an orange and a tangerine. The orange weighed $\frac{3}{4}$ pound. The tangerine weighed $\frac{4}{6}$ pound. Which was heavier? Write an inequality to show how their weights compare. (11-6)

1		
$\frac{1}{4}$	$\frac{1}{4}$	$\frac{1}{4}$

$\frac{1}{6}$	$\frac{1}{6}$	$\frac{1}{6}$	$\frac{1}{6}$

_____

_____

16. Molly says that $\frac{4}{8}$ is always the same as $\frac{1}{2}$. Andrew says that $\frac{4}{8}$ and $\frac{1}{2}$ are equivalent fractions, but they could be different amounts. Use the models below to determine which student is correct. Explain. (11-8)

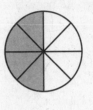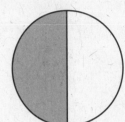

_____

_____

_____

_____

_____

_____

_____

_____

1. One way to show $\frac{7}{8}$ is $\frac{3}{8} + \frac{4}{8}$. Which of the following is another way to show $\frac{7}{8}$? (12-10)

   A $\frac{3}{8} + \frac{2}{8}$

   B $\frac{2}{8} + \frac{6}{8}$

   C $\frac{6}{8} + \frac{3}{8}$

   D $\frac{5}{8} + \frac{2}{8}$

2. On Tuesday, $\frac{2}{8}$ of the students in a class wore jeans. What fraction of the class did NOT wear jeans? (12-3)

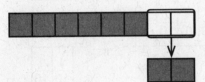

   A $\frac{9}{10}$

   B $\frac{3}{4}$

   C $\frac{6}{16}$

   D $\frac{1}{4}$

3. Milos and Asha are doing their homework. Milos has finished $\frac{3}{6}$ of his. Asha has finished $\frac{1}{6}$ of hers. How much more homework has Milos finished than Asha? (12-4)

   A $\frac{3}{6} - \frac{1}{6} = \frac{2}{6} = \frac{1}{3}$

   B $\frac{3}{6} - \frac{1}{6} = \frac{2}{0}$

   C $\frac{3}{6} + \frac{1}{6} = \frac{4}{6} = \frac{2}{3}$

   D $\frac{3}{6} + \frac{1}{6} = \frac{4}{12} = \frac{1}{3}$

4. What is the sum of $1\frac{3}{12} + 2\frac{5}{12}$? (12-8)

   A $1\frac{3}{12}$

   B $1\frac{5}{12}$

   C $2\frac{2}{3}$

   D $3\frac{2}{3}$

5. Which equation is represented on the number line shown? (12-5)

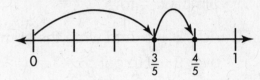

   A $\frac{3}{5} + \frac{4}{5} = \frac{7}{10}$

   B $\frac{5}{5} - \frac{3}{5} = \frac{1}{10} + \frac{2}{10} + \frac{3}{10} + \frac{4}{10}$

   C $\frac{3}{5} + \frac{1}{5} = \frac{4}{10}$

   D $\frac{3}{5} + \frac{1}{5} = \frac{4}{5}$

Name_____

6. Edna has $\frac{2}{9}$ foot of purple ribbon and $\frac{4}{9}$ foot of yellow ribbon. Which of the following can be used to find how much ribbon she has in all? (12-2)

A Add 2 + 4, and write the sum over 9 to get $\frac{6}{9}$. Simplify $\frac{6}{9}$ to $\frac{2}{3}$.

B Add 2 + 4, and write the sum over 9 + 9 to get $\frac{6}{18}$. Simplify $\frac{6}{18}$ to $\frac{1}{3}$.

C Add 2 + 4, and write the sum over 9 − 9 to get $\frac{6}{0}$.

D Add 9 + 9, and write the sum over 2 + 4 to get $\frac{18}{6}$. Simplify $\frac{18}{6}$ to 3.

7. Casey and Bret are doing their book reports. Casey has written $2\frac{5}{8}$ pages. Bret has written $\frac{6}{8}$ of a page less than Casey. How many pages has Bret written? (12-9)

_____

8. The Petersons went on a 300-mile trip. They traveled for $3\frac{5}{6}$ hours on the first day and $2\frac{2}{6}$ hours on the second day. How many hours did they travel during the first two days? (12-8)

_____

9. A soup recipe calls for $\frac{7}{8}$ cup of chicken broth and $\frac{3}{8}$ cup of cream. How much more chicken broth is needed than cream? (12-4)

_____

10. Katerina is knitting a scarf. She knit $\frac{4}{10}$ of the scarf on Monday and $\frac{2}{10}$ of the scarf on Tuesday. What fraction of the scarf has she knit? (12-1)

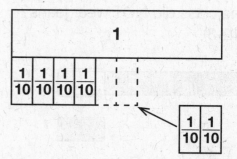

_____

11. Jean and Amy were using fraction strips to add. Jean added $\frac{1}{5} + \frac{3}{5} + \frac{4}{5}$ and found the sum $1\frac{3}{5}$. Amy said Jean must be wrong because she added $\frac{2}{5} + \frac{3}{5} + \frac{3}{5}$ and she also found the sum $1\frac{3}{5}$. Is Amy correct in her thinking? Explain. (12-10)

_____

_____

_____

_____

12. What mixed number does this model show? (12-6)

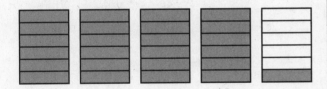

_____

13. Ricky needs $3\frac{1}{4}$ cups of sugar to make muffins. He already has $2\frac{2}{4}$ cups. How many more cups of sugar does he need? (12-9)

_____

14. What is the sum of $2\frac{5}{6} + 1\frac{2}{6}$? (12-7)

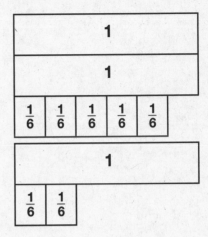

_____

15. Avi watches a movie that is $2\frac{1}{4}$ hours long. Jenae watches a movie that is $1\frac{3}{4}$ hours long. How much longer is Avi's movie? Simplify, if possible. (12-7)

_____

16. Dena is biking down a $\frac{7}{8}$-mile bike trail. She stops to greet a friend after biking $\frac{3}{8}$ of a mile. How much farther does she need to travel? Draw a picture and write an equation to solve. (12-11)

_____

_____

_____

_____

Name_____

Mark the best answer.

1. Three of the 5 students in Wayne's reading club are girls. What decimal represents $\frac{3}{5}$? (13-6)

   A 0.15

   B 0.20

   C 0.60

   D 0.75

2. What decimal is shown in the grid below? (13-7)

   A 7.41

   B 1.74

   C 1.53

   D 1.47

3. Tracy measured the mass of four samples in a science lab. Which shows the masses in order from the least to the greatest? (13-8)

   A 3.07, 3.28, 3.38, 3.1

   B 3.38, 3.28, 3.10, 3.07

   C 3.10, 3.07, 3.28, 3.38

   D 3.07, 3.10, 3.28, 3.38

4. Which statement is true? (13-8)

   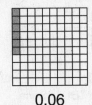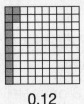

   0.06   0.12

   A 0.12 < 0.06

   B 0.06 > 0.12

   C 0.06 = 0.12

   D 0.06 < 0.12

5. What is 1.23 written as a fraction or mixed number? (13-4)

   A $\frac{1}{23}$

   B $\frac{23}{100}$

   C $1\frac{87}{100}$

   D $1\frac{23}{100}$

6. Which number is best represented by point R on the number line? (13-5)

   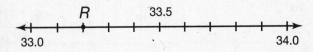

   A 33.2

   B 33.5

   C 33.6

   D 33.7

Name_____

7. What is the missing number? (13-9)

$8.36 = 8$ dollars $+ \boxed{}$ dimes $+$ 6 pennies

$8.36 = 8$ ones $+ \boxed{}$ tenths $+$ 6 hundredths

A 2

B 3

C 6

D 8

8. What is 0.41 written as a fraction? (13-4)

_____

9. Find the missing values for the multiplication equation $\frac{9}{10} = \Box \times \frac{\Box}{10}$. (13-1)

_____

10. What fraction is best represented by point C on the number line? (13-5)

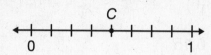

_____

11. Hal wants to make a $2\frac{1}{2}$-foot banner from a 5-foot length of cloth. If he has marked 2.0 on the cloth, what does he have to do to find $2\frac{1}{2}$ feet? (13-10)

_____

12. Write a multiplication equation with a whole number and a fraction that describes the model shown. (13-2)

| $\frac{1}{8}$ | $\frac{1}{8}$ | $\frac{1}{8}$ | $\frac{1}{8}$ | $\frac{1}{8}$ | $\frac{1}{8}$ | $\frac{1}{8}$ | $\frac{1}{8}$ | $\frac{1}{8}$ |

$\frac{3}{8}$ $\frac{3}{8}$ $\frac{3}{8}$

_____

13. Carlos is baking banana bread. He uses $\frac{3}{8}$ cup of brown sugar in one loaf. He is making 6 loaves of banana bread. How much brown sugar will Carlos use? (13-3)

_____

14. Franklin drew a number line from 0 to 1. To show $\frac{2}{5}$, how many parts should he divide the distance from 0 to 1? (13-10)

_____

15. Michael caught a fish that was $1\frac{7}{8}$ feet long. Which point on the number line best represents the length of the fish? (13-5)

_____

16. What is $\frac{3}{4}$ written as a decimal? (13-4)

_____

17. What fraction and decimal are represented by the shaded area? (13-6)

_____

18. How could you use the least amount of $1 bills, dimes, and pennies to pay for the soccer ball? (13-9)

_____

Name_____

Mark the best answer.

1. Which is the best estimate for the length of a house? (14-1)

   A 12 yards

   B 12 feet

   C 12 miles

   D 12 inches

2. Which is the best estimate of the capacity of a pitcher of water? (14-2)

   A 1,000 pints

   B 1 pint

   C 1 gallon

   D 1,000 gallons

3. Which is the best estimate of the mass of a basketball? (14-8)

   A 6 grams

   B 600 grams

   C 6,000 grams

   D 60 kilograms

4. The Robinson's have a turkey that weighs 14 pounds. How many ounces does the turkey weigh? (14-4)

   A 30 ounces

   B 112 ounces

   C 224 ounces

   D 448 ounces

5. Which of the following holds about 1 liter of water? (14-7)

   A spoon

   B glass

   C pot

   D eye dropper

Name_____

6. Timmy's birthday is 53 days away. Which of these is greater than 53 days? (14-10)

   A 3 weeks

   B 2,400 hours

   C 1 month

   D 240 hours

7. Mike, Liz, and Danna are friends. They each measured the length of the sidewalk in front of their school for a project. Which friend do you think measured incorrectly? (14-5)

Friend	Measurement
Mike	280 inches
Liz	24 feet
Danna	8 yards

   A Liz

   B Danna

   C Mike

   D All measured correctly

8. What metric unit would best measure the width of a textbook? (14-6)

   _____

9. What unit would best measure the weight of a large dog? (14-3)

   _____

10. What symbol makes the comparison true? (14-4)

   9 ft $\bigcirc$ 2 yd

   _____

11. Angela's solo in the school musical lasted 157 seconds. What symbol makes the comparison true? (14-10)

   157 seconds $\bigcirc$ 3 minutes

   _____

12. John ran 600 meters at baseball practice. How many centimeters did he run? (14-9)

_____

13. Which symbol makes the comparison true? (14-9)

200 g ◯ 2 kg

_____

14. At 2:30 P.M. the thermometer outside of Sharlene's window read 44°C. It had risen 3° between noon and 2:30 P.M. and 12° between 7:00 A.M. and noon. What was the temperature at 7:00 A.M.? (14-11)

_____

15. In 2009, 40 years had gone by since the first man walked on the moon. How many months are in 40 years? (14-10)

_____

16. Mia counted the number of quilt squares she had. She placed the squares in one long line. She counted 27 squares. How many centimeters long was Mia's line of squares? (14-6)

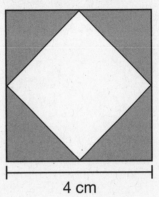

4 cm

_____

17. Cara hiked the two trails shown below on Saturday. Cara told her little sister that she had hiked 6,500 meters in one day. Is that the number of meters Cara hiked? Explain. (14-9)

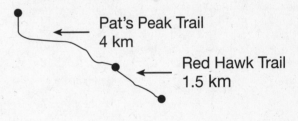

Pat's Peak Trail
4 km

Red Hawk Trail
1.5 km

_____

_____

Name_____

Mark the best answer.

1. Ricky is painting wooden blocks. He paints the top and bottom grey and the other 4 sides white. If he paints 50 blocks, how many more sides will he have painted white than grey? (15-5)

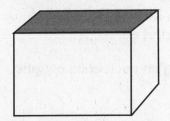

   A 100

   B 120

   C 150

   D 200

2. Which statement is true about the bedrooms below? (15-1)

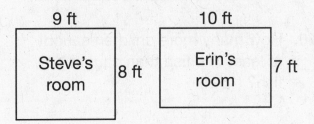

   A Erin's room has a greater area.

   B Steve's room has a greater perimeter.

   C They both have the same area.

   D They both have the same perimeter.

3. Nicole buys three juices to share with her friends. The total cost is $5.25. She pays with a $20 bill. How much change should she get back? (15-3)

   A $14.25

   B $14.75

   C $16.50

   D $18.25

4. The highway department is putting up new mile marker signs. They put up one sign per mile. One highway is 53 miles long. There is a mile marker at the start of the highway and at the end of the highway. How many mile marker signs does the highway department put up? (15-2)

   A 51 signs

   B 52 signs

   C 53 signs

   D 54 signs

5. Ed is retiling a pool that is 12 feet long and 7 feet wide. What is the area of the floor of the pool? (15-1)

   A 19 square feet

   B 42 square feet

   C 72 square feet

   D 84 square feet

Name_____

6. Ben played at a friend's house for 2 hours 35 minutes. Later he played at a park. He played for 3 hours 52 minutes in all that day. How long did he play at the park? (15-2)

_____

7. Lisa buys 4 postcards, a t-shirt, and a button on a field trip to Washington, DC. They cost a total of $23.19 from the gift shop. She paid for them with 3 $10 bills. How much change should she get back? (15-3)

_____

8. A picture frame measures 5 inches wide and 7 inches long. What is the perimeter of the frame? (15-1)

_____

For problems **9** and **10,** use the data and the line plot below.

A summer camp had a fishing competition. The camp counselor checked with each of the children to find how many fish each caught. Their totals were: 2, 1, 0, 3, 2, 0, 4, 0, 1, 2, 0, 5, 0, 3, 0, 1, 0, 2, 1, 2, and 4.

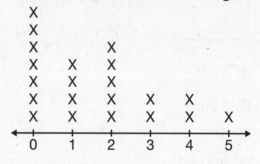

Number of fish each child caught

9. How many fish did the children catch in all? (15-4)

_____

10. How many more children caught at least one fish than caught no fish? (15-4)

_____

Name_____

11. The measurements of Norton's computer screen are shown below. What is the perimeter of his screen? (15-1)

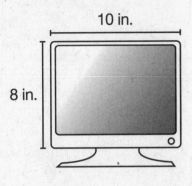

10 in.

8 in.

_____

12. Travis is making a pattern with triangle tiles like below. Each side of a triangle is 3 inches long. What is the perimeter when the pattern has 36 triangles? (15-5)

_____

Number of Triangles	1	4	9	16
Perimeter	9 in.	18 in.	27 in.	36 in.

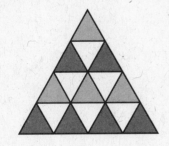

13. Jared is placing chairs around a rectangular stage. The stage is 10 feet long and 22 feet wide. He wants to put a chair at each corner and every 2 feet along the sides. How many chairs will Jared need for his stage? (15-5)

_____

14. Belinda uses drink mix to make a 2-quart pitcher of lemonade. She has a can of drink mix that makes 3 gallons. How many pitchers can she make? (15-2)

_____

Name_____

Mark the best answer.

1. Which triangle has 3 equal sides? (16-8)

   A isosceles

   B scalene

   C straight

   D equilateral

2. Which polygon has less than 4 vertices? (16-7)

   A pentagon

   B quadrilateral

   C triangle

   D hexagon

3. Malcolm used 4 sticks to build a two-dimensional figure with at least one set of parallel sides, and at least one set of perpendicular sides. Which could be his figure? (16-1)

   A

   B

   C

   D

4. Which geometric term best describes a checker on a checkerboard? (16-2)

   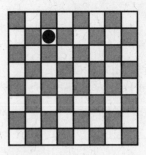

   A point

   B ray

   C line segment

   D plane

5. Which type of quadrilateral always has 4 right angles? (16-9)

   A square

   B rhombus

   C trapezoid

   D parallelogram

Name_____

6. Iris picked the following shapes out of a bag.

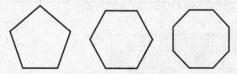

She said the shapes did not belong with the ones Manny chose, below.

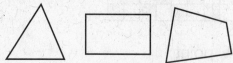

Which is the best description of the shapes Iris chose? (16-11)

A polygons with more than 4 sides

B polygons with parallel sides

C polygons with acute angles

D polygons with a right angle

7. Tom put 5 toothpicks in the pattern below. Which toothpick is parallel to toothpick *U*? (16-1)

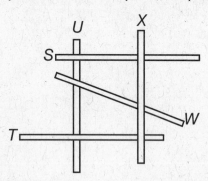

_____

8. What type of angle is shown below? (16-2)

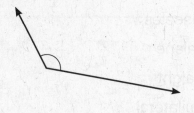

_____

9. How many sides does an octagon have? (16-7)

_____

10. Whose shape has only 2 lines of symmetry? (16-10)

Tina	Sara
△	☐
Scott	Jake
▭	△

_____

Name_____

11. What is the measure of the angle shown below? (16-5)

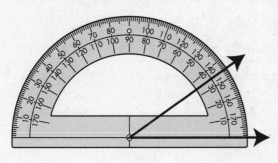

_____

12. Gabriela cuts a pecan pie into 9 pieces of the same size. What is the angle measure of each piece? (16-3)

_____

13. What is the measure of the angle shown below? (16-4)

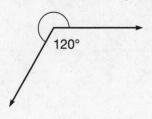

120°

_____

14. If the measure of ∠QRS is 90° and the measure of ∠SRT is 27°, what is the measure of ∠TRQ? (16-6)

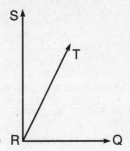

_____

Name_____

Mark the best answer.

1. Which has the same value as 5×7?

A $7 + 7 + 7 + 7 + 7$

B $5 + 5 + 5 + 5 + 5$

C $5 + 7$

D $7 + 7 + 7 + 7 + 7 + 5$

2. Each bike has two tires.

If Shannon counted the tires in groups of 2, which list shows numbers she could have named?

A 12, 14, 17, 20

B 8, 12, 16, 21

C 15, 17, 20, 22

D 12, 14, 16, 18

3. Which number sentence is true?

A $2 \div 8 = 4$

B $0 \div 4 = 1$

C $1 \div 2 = 2$

D $0 \div 1 = 0$

4. Which number makes the number sentence true?

$8 \times 7 = \boxed{} \times 8$

A 1

B 7

C 8

D 9

5. Jen lived in five different houses growing up. Below are the five numbers of the houses where she lived. If the pattern continues, what are the next three numbers of the houses she will live in?

21, 28, 35, 42, 49, $\boxed{}$, $\boxed{}$, $\boxed{}$

A 56, 62, 72

B 56, 63, 70

C 55, 63, 70

D 63, 70, 77

6. Darnell has 4 photo albums. Each album has 8 photos. How many photos does Darnell have?

A 12 photos

B 28 photos

C 32 photos

D 36 photos

Name_____

7. Which numeral makes both number sentences true?

$6 \times \boxed{} = 42$

$42 \div 6 = \boxed{}$

A 8

B 7

C 6

D 5

8. Which number sentence is in the same fact family as the one below?

$27 \div 9 = \boxed{}$

A $9 \times \boxed{} = 27$

B $9 + \boxed{} = 27$

C $27 - \boxed{} = 9$

D $27 + 9 = \boxed{}$

9. The numbers below form a pattern.

2, 4, 8, 16, 32, …

What is a rule for this pattern?

A Add 2

B Subtract 2

C Multiply by 2

D Multiply by 4

10. Jamal is playing a number game. He needs to complete the pattern below to win.

1, 1, 2, 1, 1, 2, 1, 1, …

What are the next three numbers in the pattern?

A 2, 2, 2,

B 2, 1, 2

C 2, 1, 1

D 1, 1, 1

11. Gina wrote the pattern below in her notebook.

300, 280, 260, 240, 220, …

What is the next number in Gina's pattern?

A 200

B 210

C 220

D 240

12. Emily read a 210-page book in 7 days. She read the same number of pages each day. Which number sentence shows how to find the number of pages Emily read each day?

A $210 + 7 = \boxed{}$

B $210 - 7 = \boxed{}$

C $210 \times 7 = \boxed{}$

D $210 \div 7 = \boxed{}$

Name_____

13. One spider has 8 legs. How many legs do three spiders have? Use the table below to solve.

Number of Spiders	Number of Legs
1	8
2	16
3	
4	32

  A 8

  B 21

  C 24

  D 40

14. Roger is measuring the perimeter around squares of different sizes. If the pattern continues, what will the perimeter around a square with 5-inch sides be?

2 in.   3 in.   4 in.

Length of each side	2	3	4	5
Perimeter		8	12	16	

  A 5 inches

  B 10 inches

  C 15 inches

  D 20 inches

15. What is the number below written in standard form?

900,000 + 10,000 + 4,000 + 700 + 30

  A 9,473

  B 91,473

  C 914,730

  D 9,147,300

16. What is the value of the 5 in 3,156?

  A 5,000

  B 500

  C 50

  D 5

17. Which symbol makes the statement true?

1,478 ☐ 1,492

  A >

  B <

  C =

  D +

18. Which list shows the numbers in order from least to greatest?

A 1,105   1,155   1,205   1,502

B 1,105   2,205   1,155   1,502

C 2,205   1,155   1,502   1,105

D 1,502   2,205   1,155   1,105

19. Jessie read 56 pages in her book on Monday and 89 pages on Tuesday. Jessie used compensation as shown below to find 56 + 89. What is the missing number?

$$56 + 89 = \boxed{} + 90 = 145$$

A 54

B 55

C 60

D 85

20. On Friday, 2,524 shoppers visited a mall. On Saturday, 3,121 shoppers went to the same mall. What is the best way to estimate how many more shoppers were at the mall on Saturday?

A 3,100 − 2,400 = 700

B 3,130 − 2,520 = 610

C 3,120 − 2,520 = 600

D 3,120 − 2,500 = 620

21. At the baseball stadium, 10,265 cars can park in the parking lot. At the football stadium, 12,898 cars can park. How many cars can park in all?

A 22,053

B 22,163

C 22,153

D 23,163

22. Jerry had 1,272 baseball cards. He donated 685 of them to a children's hospital. How many baseball cards does he have left?

A 587 baseball cards

B 613 baseball cards

C 693 baseball cards

D 1,487 baseball cards

23. The Anderson family drove 2,060 miles on a trip to Omaha, Nebraska. The next year, they drove 1,787 miles on a trip to Louisville, Kentucky. How many more miles did they drive on their Omaha trip?

A 273 miles   **C** 373 miles

B 283 miles   **D** 1,283 miles

24. What is 1,760 rounded to the nearest thousand?

A 2,000   **C** 1,500

B 1,800   **D** 1,000

Name_____

Mark the best answer.

1. What is the product of 3 × 10?

  A 300

  B 33

  C 30

  D 3

2. Which expression shows breaking apart to find 4 × 36?

  A (4 × 300) + (4 × 6)

  B (4 × 40) + (4 × 4)

  C (4 × 35) + (4 × 5)

  D (4 × 30) + (4 × 6)

3. To find the product of 7 × 62 using compensation, Kerry first multiplied 7 × 60 = 420. What should Kerry do next?

  A 420 + 7 = 427

  B 420 − 7 = 413

  C 420 + 14 = 434

  D 420 − 14 = 406

4. Tara teaches 4 classes, each with 29 students. What is a reasonable estimate of the total number of students in Tara's 4 classes?

  A 300

  B 120

  C 30

  D 12

5. A ream of paper has 500 sheets. How many sheets are in 5 reams of paper?

  A 1,000

  B 2,500

  C 5,000

  D 5,500

6. Mr. Sanchez gives 5 tours of the Grand Canyon each day. If there are 18 people in every tour group, how many people will Mr. Sanchez guide in one day?

  A 23

  B 80

  C 85

  D 90

Name_____

7. Look at the array and calculation below.

What calculation was used to give the partial product 40?

A 2 × 20

B 4 × 4

C 4 × 10

D 14 × 10

8. A student made 8 round trips traveling to and from college. If each round trip was 214 miles, about how many miles did the student drive in all?

A 200

B 400

C 2,000

D 4,000

9. A horse weighs 1,097 pounds. A white rhino weighs 4 times as much as the horse. How much does the rhino weigh?

A 4,388 pounds

B 4,088 pounds

C 3,048 pounds

D 1,388 pounds

10. In one week, 678 cars are washed at City Car Wash. If the same number of cars are washed each week, how many cars are washed in 5 weeks?

A 3,390

B 3,040

C 2,800

D 2,678

11. To find 40 × 600, Maria first found 4 × 6 = 24. How many zeros should Maria include in the product?

A 1

B 2

C 3

D 4

12. Cara filled 28 pages in a photo album. If she put 4 pictures on each page, how many pictures are in the album?

A 32 pictures

B 56 pictures

C 112 pictures

D 220 pictures

13. The cafeteria sold 45 salads, 28 cheese sandwiches, and 4 times as many ham sandwiches as cheese sandwiches. How many sandwiches were sold?

A 185   **C** 112

B 140   **D** 73

14. There are 13 girls on Janelle's soccer team. Uniforms cost $32 each. Which equation uses estimation correctly to show about how much money the team spent?

A $5 \times \$35 = \$175$

B $10 \times \$30 = \$300$

C $20 \times \$30 = \$600$

D $20 \times \$32 = \$640$

15. Use the grid below to find the product of 20×18.

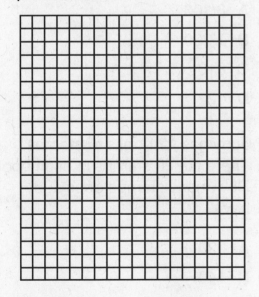

A 320   **C** 360

B 340   **D** 380

16. Mark's football team has scored about 23 points each game. They played 12 games this season. What is the best estimate for the total number of points they scored in the season?

A 350

B 230

C 100

D 23

17. Tony can make 40 meatballs with one package of meat. If he uses 10 packages, how many meatballs can he make?

A 100

B 400

C 500

D 1,000

18. Ms. Jones drinks 10 glasses of water every day. How many glasses of water will she drink in 30 days?

A 10

B 100

C 300

D 400

Name_____

19. Which number is missing from the table?

	10	5
30	300	
7	70	35

A 150

B 185

C 350

D 490

20. Mr. Sun's students are using part of their field trip fund to see a play. The tickets cost $12 each. If 23 students go, how much will the class spend on tickets?

A $216

B $230

C $253

D $276

21. Raul's dad bakes bread 5 days a week. If he bakes 85 loaves each day, how many loaves of bread will his dad bake in two 5-day work weeks?

A 850

B 595

C 425

D 400

22. Ani used the array to find the product of 13 × 18.

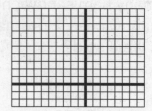

Which partial products should Ani add to find the product?

A 1 + 1 + 3 + 8

B 3 + 8 + 10 + 10

C 24 + 30 + 30 + 60

D 24 + 30 + 80 + 100

23. For a special recycling project, 20 classes worked to collect 61 pounds of newspaper each. How many total pounds of newspaper were collected?

A 8,100

B 1,220

C 810

D 122

24. Judy has 12 books of stamps. There are 20 stamps in each book. How many stamps does Judy have?

A 120

B 140

C 240

D 260

Name_____

Mark the best answer.

1. Luisa has 417 beans. She has 7 jars in which to store the beans. How can she use estimation to find about how many beans to put in each jar?

   A Round the number of jars to 10

   B Round the number of beans to 410

   C Round the number of beans to 415

   D Round the number of beans to 420

2. A total of 150 students are in the fourth grade at Mockingbird School. There are 5 classes, each with the same number of students. What basic fact can you use to help solve the problem?

   A $15 \times 5 = 75$

   B $15 \div 5 = 3$

   C $15 - 5 = 10$

   D $15 + 5 = 20$

3. Ms. Mitchell uses 186 tubes of paint to make supply packs for her art class. She puts 8 tubes in each pack. How many supply packs will she make, and how many tubes of paint will be left over?

   A 20 packs, 6 left over

   B 22 packs, 3 left over

   C 23 packs, 1 left over

   D 23 packs, 2 left over

4. Maria bought 50 tulip bulbs. She planted the bulbs in rows with 8 bulbs in each row. Which model shows both the correct number of rows and left over bulbs?

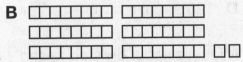

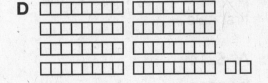

5. Jose has 396 trading cards. If he puts the cards into 8 albums, estimate how many cards he will have in each album.

   A About 30 cards

   B About 45 cards

   C About 50 cards

   D About 55 cards

6. Jason counted 284 marbles in a bag. If each bag contains the same number of marbles, how many marbles would be in 6 bags?

   A 1,684   C 1,884

   B 1,704   D 1,948

7. Nikki has 96 sequins to sew on a flag. She wants to sew them in 6 rows. How many sequins should she sew in each row?

A 16 sequins

B 20 sequins

C 90 sequins

D 120 sequins

8. Miguel's scout division raised money for a camping trip. They earned a total of $1,498 at 7 bake sales. They earned the same amount at each sale. How much money did they make at the first sale?

A $214

B $208

C $176

D $112

9. Joey used 154 craft sticks to make puppets. He used one pair of craft sticks for each puppet. How many puppets did Joey make?

A 77 puppets

B 154 puppets

C 308 puppets

D Not here

10. Which list shows the fractions below in order from least to greatest?

$\frac{1}{8}$	$\frac{1}{8}$	$\frac{1}{8}$

$\frac{1}{3}$

$\frac{1}{2}$

A $\frac{1}{3}, \frac{1}{2}, \frac{3}{8}$

B $\frac{1}{3}, \frac{3}{8}, \frac{1}{2}$

C $\frac{1}{2}, \frac{3}{8}, \frac{1}{3}$

D $\frac{3}{8}, \frac{1}{3}, \frac{1}{2}$

11. Which list shows all the factors of 38?

A 1, 38

B 1, 2, 38

C 1, 2, 16, 38

D 1, 2, 19, 38

12. Which 2 fractions are examples of equivalent fractions?

A $\frac{2}{8}, \frac{1}{4}$

B $\frac{3}{16}, \frac{1}{4}$

C $\frac{5}{12}, \frac{1}{3}$

D $\frac{7}{16}, \frac{3}{4}$

13. The 2 plates of pizza below show what was left after the Chavez family finished dinner.

 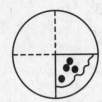

Which of the following compares the portion of pizza left on each plate?

A $\frac{3}{8} > \frac{1}{4}$

B $\frac{3}{8} < \frac{1}{4}$

C $\frac{3}{8} = \frac{1}{4}$

D $\frac{3}{4} > \frac{5}{8}$

14. What generalization can be made about all multiples of 4?

A They are all odd

B They are all multiples of 2

C They are all factors of 5

D They are both even and odd

15. Where would the first digit of the quotient be placed in the division problem below?

$$8\overline{)592}$$

A Above the 9

B Above the 5

C Above the 8

D Above the 2

16. Use the model below. What is the sum of $\frac{3}{8}$ and $\frac{2}{8}$?

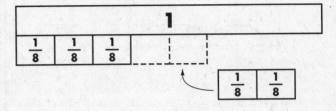

A $\frac{2}{8}$

B $\frac{3}{8}$

C $\frac{5}{8}$

D $\frac{7}{8}$

17. Monday night Tyrell spent $\frac{2}{6}$ hour on his homework and Eva spent $\frac{5}{6}$ hour on her homework. How much more time did Eva spend on homework than Tyrell?

A $\frac{3}{6}$ hour

B $\frac{2}{6}$ hour

C $\frac{1}{6}$ hour

D $1\frac{1}{6}$ hours

18. What is the sum of $\frac{7}{12} + \frac{3}{12}$?

A $\frac{11}{12}$

B $\frac{10}{12}$

C $\frac{9}{12}$

D $\frac{8}{12}$

19. The number line shows which of the following equations?

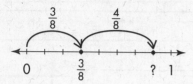

A $\frac{4}{4} - \frac{3}{4} = \frac{1}{4}$

B $\frac{3}{8} + \frac{4}{8} = \frac{7}{8}$

C $\frac{1}{8} + \frac{4}{8} = \frac{5}{8}$

D $\frac{7}{8} - \frac{4}{8} = \frac{3}{8}$

20. Ken ate $\frac{5}{3}$ containers of yogurt. What is $\frac{5}{3}$ expressed as a mixed number?

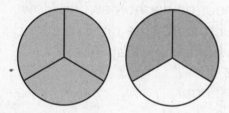

A $5\frac{1}{3}$ **C** $1\frac{2}{3}$

B $2\frac{3}{5}$ **D** $1\frac{1}{3}$

21. Mike needs $1\frac{4}{8}$ cups of flour to make a cake and $1\frac{7}{8}$ cups of flour to make a piecrust. How much flour does Mike need to bake the cake and piecrust? Use the model to find the sum.

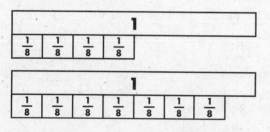

A $1\frac{3}{8}$ cups   **C** $2\frac{8}{10}$ cups

B 2 cups   **D** $3\frac{3}{8}$ cups

22. What is the difference of $2\frac{3}{8} - 1\frac{7}{8}$?

A $\frac{1}{8}$

B $\frac{3}{8}$

C $\frac{1}{2}$

D $1\frac{1}{2}$

23. Which of the following is another way to show $\frac{7}{10}$?

A $\frac{3}{10} + \frac{2}{10} + \frac{1}{10} + \frac{1}{10}$

B $\frac{3}{5} + \frac{4}{5}$

C $\frac{7}{10} + \frac{1}{10}$

D $\frac{3}{10} + \frac{3}{10} + \frac{3}{10}$

24. Jan drew the number line below.

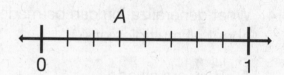

Which of the following is equivalent to Point A?

A $\frac{3}{10}$

B $\frac{1}{2}$

C $\frac{4}{8}$

D $\frac{3}{8}$

Name_____

Mark the best answer.

1. What is the best estimate of how much an apple weighs?

   A About 1 ounce

   B About 6 ounces

   C About 1 pound

   D About 5 tons

2. Larry measures an object's mass in grams. Which of the following objects is he most likely measuring?

   A A frog

   B A watermelon

   C A surfboard

   D A horse

3. Lara's bed is 5 feet long. How many inches long is the bed?

   A 1 yard

   B 48 inches

   C 60 inches

   D 72 inches

4. In 2007, Oklahoma celebrated its 100th birthday. How many months are in 100 years?

   A 600 months

   B 1,200 months

   C 1,800 months

   D 2,400 months

5. Which figure below has two lines of symmetry?

 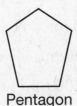

Octagon   Pentagon

Rectangle   Triangle

   A Octagon   **C** Rectangle

   B Pentagon   **D** Triangle

6. Diego made an example of an equilateral triangle. Which triangle could be Diego's drawing?

   A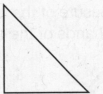

   B

   C

   D

Name_____

7. Which measure is equal to 3 liters?

   A 3 mL

   B 30 mL

   C 300 mL

   D 3,000 mL

8. Look at the clock below.

What kind of angle do the hands form?

   A Acute

   B Right

   C Obtuse

   D Straight

9. What is the measure of the angle formed by the hands of the clock?

   A 45°

   B 90°

   C 180°

   D 360°

10. What are all the names that could be used for the shape below?

   A Quadrilateral, parallelogram

   B Quadrilateral, trapezoid, rectangle

   C Quadrilateral, parallelogram, rhombus

   D Quadrilateral, parallelogram, square

11. Thomas drew a pair of perpendicular lines. Which of the following could be his drawing?

A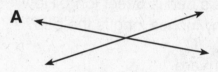

B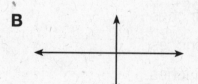

C

D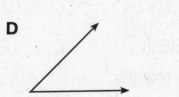

12. Look at the number line below.

What decimal and fraction are shown by the point marked on the number line?

A 0.1, $\frac{1}{10}$

B 0.3, $\frac{3}{10}$

C 0.3, $\frac{1}{3}$

D 0.5, $\frac{1}{2}$

13. Remy wanted to measure the angle of the slide in the playground. He used a piece of folded paper that was 10°. He measured that 3 of the folded paper angles would fit in the angle made by the slide. What was the angle of the slide?

A 75°

B 60°

C 45°

D 30°

14. A packet of spices contains 0.52 ounces of garlic powder, 0.36 ounces of salt, 0.6 ounces of red pepper flakes, and 0.25 ounces of oregano. Which spice does the packet have the most of?

A Garlic powder

B Salt

C Red pepper flakes

D Oregano

15. What is the correct way to represent 2 dollars + 5 dimes + 8 pennies using a dollar sign and decimal point?

A $0.258

B $2.58

C $2.85

D $8.52

16. Which of the following shows $\frac{3}{8}$ as a multiple of a unit fraction?

A 3×8

B $\frac{3}{8} + \frac{1}{8}$

C $\frac{3}{8} \times \frac{1}{8}$

D $3 \times \frac{1}{8}$

17. Joy jogs $\frac{1}{2}$ mile 3 times a week. How far does Joy jog in one week?

A $3\frac{1}{2}$ miles

B $1\frac{1}{2}$ miles

C $\frac{2}{3}$ mile

D $\frac{1}{6}$ mile

18. Find $7 \times \frac{1}{3}$.

A $\frac{1}{21}$

B $\frac{3}{7}$

C $2\frac{1}{3}$

D $7\frac{1}{3}$

Name_____

19. The perimeter of the rectangle shown below is 28 cm.

6 cm

What is the area of the rectangle?

A 12 square centimeters

B 14 square centimeters

C 36 square centimeters

D 48 square centimeters

20. The cooking instructions for a pie say to bake it for 1 hour and 35 minutes. The pie has already baked for 50 minutes. How many more minutes does the pie need to bake?

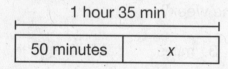

1 hour 35 min

| 50 minutes | x |

A 45 minutes

B 35 minutes

C 25 minutes

D 15 minutes

21. Eugene used a $15 gift card to buy a digital music album. The cost of the album was $12.89. How much did Eugene have remaining on his gift card?

A $3.89   **C** $2.11

B $3.09   **D** $2.09

22. Nancy made a line plot to keep track of the number of homework assignments she received each week.

Homework Assignments Per Week

```
            X
            X       X
  X         X   X X                 X
  X         X   X X   X   X X   X   X
  X X   X   X X X X X X X   X X X
  ←—+—+—+—+—+—+—+—+—+—+—+—+—+—+—+—+→
  5       10      15      20
```

How many assignments did Nancy receive the most number of times?

A 8   **C** 15

B 11   **D** 20

23. Ron drew an angle that measured 160°. Then he drew a ray that divided the angle in half. What is the measure of each of the new angles formed?

A 180°

B 160°

C 80°

D 60°

24. Collin solved a math problem and got an answer of $\frac{6}{10}$. He wants to write the fraction as a decimal. Which decimal should he write?

A 6.0

B 0.66

C 6.10

D 0.6

Name_____

Mark the best answer.

1. During the 2008 Summer Olympics in Beijing, Poland won 10 medals. France won 4 times as many medals as Poland.

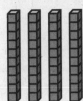

How many medals did France win?

A 14

B 40

C 44

D 400

2. Which shape below has only 1 line of symmetry?

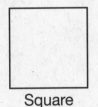

Square   Pentagon

Rectangle   Triangle

A Square

B Pentagon

C Rectangle

D Triangle

3. What is the difference of $\frac{4}{8} - \frac{3}{8}$?

A $\frac{7}{8}$

B $\frac{7}{16}$

C $\frac{12}{16}$

D $\frac{1}{8}$

4. A skyscraper has 412 windows. A window washer cleaned 285. How can he find the number of windows left to clean?

412 windows in all

| 285 | ? |

A Multiply 412 by 16.

B Multiply 285 by 412.

C Subtract 285 from 412.

D Add 412 to 285.

5. Nadia burned 56 calories practicing martial arts. She burned 8 calories each minute.

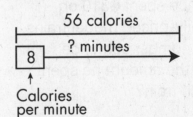

Which number sentence can be used to find how many minutes Nadia practiced martial arts?

A $56 \div 8 = \square$

B $56 - 8 = \square$

C $56 + 8 = \square$

D $56 \times 8 = \square$

Name_____

6. The American flag has 50 white stars and 13 red and white stripes. In a parade, 17 people are waving small American flags as they march by. How many stars are on the flags in all?

A 221

B 650

C 850

D 945

7. What decimal is shown in the grid below?

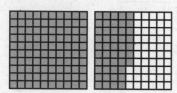

A 2.47

B 1.74

C 1.47

D 1.04

8. Lawrence spent $310 on 5 equally-priced model trains. Which number sentence shows the amount he spent for each train?

A $300 ÷ 5 = $60

B $310 ÷ 5 = $62

C 5 × $310 = $1,860

D 5 × $300 = $1,500

9. Kevin measured that it was 45 feet from the door of his classroom to the principal's office. What is that distance in yards?

A 3 yards

B 15 yards

C 42 yards

D 135 yards

10. Andy jumped 1.2 meters in a track contest. Which point on the number line below represents the number 1.2?

A R

B S

C T

D U

11. Kelly's class collected 3,129 pennies in 7 months. If they collected the same number of pennies each month, how many pennies did they collect in one month?

A 304 R1

B 407

C 432 R5

D 447

Name_____

12. Wanda painted $\frac{2}{8}$ of a poster. Which number should go in the box to make another fraction that is equivalent to $\frac{2}{8}$?

$$\frac{2}{8} = \frac{1}{\square}$$

A 2

B 4

C 6

D 16

13. The Singapore Flyer, in China, is one of the world's largest Ferris wheels. There are 28 cars on the Ferris wheel and each car can hold 28 passengers. About how many passengers can ride the Ferris wheel at one time?

A 60

B 400

C 625

D 900

14. Which fraction is **NOT** equivalent to the shaded area of the rectangle?

A $\frac{1}{2}$

B $\frac{3}{5}$

C $\frac{6}{10}$

D $\frac{60}{100}$

15. Which of the following has a 2 in the hundredths place?

A 16.29

B 18.32

C 22.83

D 539.2

16. A helicopter landing pad measures 11 meters wide and 15 meters long. What is the perimeter of the pad?

A 26 meters

B 52 meters

C 165 meters

D 2,475 meters

17. Norma measured the length and width of the placemat shown.

12 inches

9 inches

What is the area of the rectangular placemat?

A 21 square inches

B 42 square inches

C 98 square inches

D 108 square inches

18. The food pantry sets a goal of collecting 40 cans of food each day in November. There are 30 days in November. If the food pantry reaches its goal, how many cans of food will be collected during November?

  A   120

  B   1,200

  C   1,240

  D 12,000

19. Jorge saw that the clock hands formed an angle.

Which angle measure best describes the angle formed by the clock hands?

  A About 45°

  B About 90°

  C About 180°

  D About 360°

20. What is $1\frac{3}{5} - \frac{4}{5}$?

  A $\frac{1}{5}$

  B $\frac{3}{5}$

  C $\frac{4}{5}$

  D $2\frac{2}{5}$

21. Peter wrote the following numbers in a row.

9, 16, 23, 30

If the pattern continues, what three numbers will come next?

  A 36, 42, 48

  B 37, 44, 51

  C 37, 42, 49

  D 42, 54, 66

22. Kylie has 4 shelves. Each shelf displays 7 trophies. Which number sentence shows how many trophies are displayed in the case?

  A $4 \times 7 = 28$

  B $4 \times 3 = 12$

  C $7 - 4 = 3$

  D $7 + 3 = 10$

23. A family membership at a museum costs $85 per year. What is the total cost of 29 family memberships?

  A $885

  B $935

  C $2,325

  D $2,465

Name_____

Give each answer.

1.	5 + 6 = ____	**18.**	1 + 9 = ____	**35.**	6 − 5 = ____
2.	8 + 8 = ____	**19.**	5 + 9 = ____	**36.**	8 − 7 = ____
3.	6 + 1 = ____	**20.**	6 + 8 = ____	**37.**	15 − 8 = ____
4.	8 + 2 = ____	**21.**	2 + 7 = ____	**38.**	8 − 6 = ____
5.	4 + 3 = ____	**22.**	5 + 5 = ____	**39.**	8 − 1 = ____
6.	2 + 9 = ____	**23.**	2 + 6 = ____	**40.**	9 − 3 = ____
7.	7 + 9 = ____	**24.**	9 + 6 = ____	**41.**	2 − 1 = ____
8.	4 + 9 = ____	**25.**	4 + 6 = ____	**42.**	7 − 7 = ____
9.	6 + 6 = ____	**26.**	6 − 2 = ____	**43.**	11 − 6 = ____
10.	5 + 4 = ____	**27.**	11 − 9 = ____	**44.**	7 − 2 = ____
11.	2 + 8 = ____	**28.**	9 − 6 = ____	**45.**	5 − 4 = ____
12.	7 + 3 = ____	**29.**	7 − 4 = ____	**46.**	12 − 8 = ____
13.	8 + 3 = ____	**30.**	8 − 5 = ____	**47.**	14 − 9 = ____
14.	4 + 8 = ____	**31.**	6 − 4 = ____	**48.**	13 − 5 = ____
15.	9 + 9 = ____	**32.**	10 − 3 = ____	**49.**	11 − 4 = ____
16.	3 + 9 = ____	**33.**	8 − 8 = ____	**50.**	10 − 7 = ____
17.	7 + 7 = ____	**34.**	18 − 9 = ____		

Name_____

Give each answer.

1. $6 + 6 =$ _____
2. $10 - 2 =$ _____
3. $7 + 1 =$ _____
4. $7 + 3 =$ _____
5. $4 - 3 =$ _____
6. $8 + 1 =$ _____
7. $10 - 7 =$ _____
8. $13 - 6 =$ _____
9. $8 - 4 =$ _____
10. $8 + 5 =$ _____
11. $12 - 4 =$ _____
12. $7 + 3 =$ _____
13. $7 + 8 =$ _____
14. $9 + 9 =$ _____
15. $7 - 0 =$ _____
16. $10 - 6 =$ _____
17. $7 + 9 =$ _____

18. $9 - 7 =$ _____
19. $11 - 5 =$ _____
20. $7 - 1 =$ _____
21. $8 + 4 =$ _____
22. $1 + 8 =$ _____
23. $9 - 5 =$ _____
24. $14 - 7 =$ _____
25. $9 + 2 =$ _____
26. $7 + 2 =$ _____
27. $2 + 5 =$ _____
28. $8 + 6 =$ _____
29. $4 + 3 =$ _____
30. $8 + 9 =$ _____
31. $9 - 6 =$ _____
32. $4 + 4 =$ _____
33. $9 - 8 =$ _____
34. $3 + 3 =$ _____

35. $5 + 8 =$ _____
36. $12 - 3 =$ _____
37. $2 + 8 =$ _____
38. $6 - 1 =$ _____
39. $2 + 2 =$ _____
40. $7 - 4 =$ _____
41. $2 + 7 =$ _____
42. $11 - 3 =$ _____
43. $1 + 6 =$ _____
44. $3 - 3 =$ _____
45. $9 + 8 =$ _____
46. $11 - 6 =$ _____
47. $8 - 8 =$ _____
48. $16 - 9 =$ _____
49. $9 + 7 =$ _____
50. $14 - 5 =$ _____

Name_____

Give each answer.

1. $9 - 4 =$ _____	18. $10 - 5 =$ _____	35. $1 + 8 =$ _____
2. $7 + 2 =$ _____	19. $7 + 6 =$ _____	36. $16 - 8 =$ _____
3. $6 - 6 =$ _____	20. $11 - 8 =$ _____	37. $6 + 8 =$ _____
4. $2 + 1 =$ _____	21. $9 + 4 =$ _____	38. $2 + 3 =$ _____
5. $5 - 3 =$ _____	22. $3 + 8 =$ _____	39. $3 - 1 =$ _____
6. $9 - 7 =$ _____	23. $11 - 5 =$ _____	40. $4 + 5 =$ _____
7. $5 - 4 =$ _____	24. $10 - 1 =$ _____	41. $10 - 3 =$ _____
8. $4 - 4 =$ _____	25. $6 + 2 =$ _____	42. $15 - 9 =$ _____
9. $8 + 8 =$ _____	26. $9 + 2 =$ _____	43. $1 + 7 =$ _____
10. $6 + 3 =$ _____	27. $8 + 6 =$ _____	44. $12 - 9 =$ _____
11. $7 - 6 =$ _____	28. $2 + 9 =$ _____	45. $3 + 3 =$ _____
12. $6 + 5 =$ _____	29. $5 + 5 =$ _____	46. $13 - 8 =$ _____
13. $8 - 4 =$ _____	30. $4 + 7 =$ _____	47. $17 - 9 =$ _____
14. $7 + 4 =$ _____	31. $9 - 2 =$ _____	48. $9 + 6 =$ _____
15. $13 - 7 =$ _____	32. $9 + 8 =$ _____	49. $6 + 7 =$ _____
16. $15 - 6 =$ _____	33. $11 - 6 =$ _____	50. $9 + 5 =$ _____
17. $8 + 9 =$ _____	34. $6 + 9 =$ _____	

Name_____

Give each answer.

1. $4 \times 3 =$ _____

2. $7 \times 3 =$ _____

3. $5 \times 5 =$ _____

4. $2 \times 1 =$ _____

5. $3 \times 3 =$ _____

6. $8 \times 6 =$ _____

7. $9 \times 2 =$ _____

8. $3 \times 4 =$ _____

9. $5 \times 8 =$ _____

10. $9 \times 3 =$ _____

11. $2 \times 8 =$ _____

12. $3 \times 6 =$ _____

13. $2 \times 5 =$ _____

14. $0 \times 7 =$ _____

15. $5 \times 6 =$ _____

16. $2 \times 9 =$ _____

17. $8 \times 2 =$ _____

18. $5 \times 4 =$ _____

19. $9 \times 6 =$ _____

20. $2 \times 7 =$ _____

21. $8 \times 3 =$ _____

22. $7 \times 2 =$ _____

23. $3 \times 8 =$ _____

24. $6 \times 7 =$ _____

25. $7 \times 4 =$ _____

26. $5 \times 3 =$ _____

27. $1 \times 4 =$ _____

28. $7 \times 6 =$ _____

29. $6 \times 3 =$ _____

30. $7 \times 8 =$ _____

31. $8 \times 4 =$ _____

32. $6 \times 2 =$ _____

33. $4 \times 9 =$ _____

34. $5 \times 7 =$ _____

35. $3 \times 2 =$ _____

36. $6 \times 9 =$ _____

37. $9 \times 7 =$ _____

38. $2 \times 6 =$ _____

39. $8 \times 5 =$ _____

40. $6 \times 5 =$ _____

41. $4 \times 0 =$ _____

42. $9 \times 8 =$ _____

43. $5 \times 2 =$ _____

44. $7 \times 7 =$ _____

45. $5 \times 9 =$ _____

46. $2 \times 4 =$ _____

47. $9 \times 9 =$ _____

48. $4 \times 8 =$ _____

49. $6 \times 6 =$ _____

50. $7 \times 9 =$ _____

Name_____

Give each answer.

1. $3 \times 4 =$ _____

2. $9 \times 4 =$ _____

3. $7 \times 6 =$ _____

4. $4 \times 2 =$ _____

5. $8 \times 4 =$ _____

6. $6 \times 1 =$ _____

7. $3 \times 9 =$ _____

8. $8 \times 9 =$ _____

9. $6 \times 9 =$ _____

10. $8 \times 7 =$ _____

11. $4 \times 6 =$ _____

12. $3 \times 5 =$ _____

13. $2 \times 3 =$ _____

14. $2 \times 7 =$ _____

15. $7 \times 5 =$ _____

16. $7 \times 1 =$ _____

17. $1 \times 0 =$ _____

18. $2 \times 9 =$ _____

19. $7 \times 4 =$ _____

20. $9 \times 3 =$ _____

21. $8 \times 8 =$ _____

22. $6 \times 2 =$ _____

23. $3 \times 3 =$ _____

24. $9 \times 6 =$ _____

25. $1 \times 3 =$ _____

26. $9 \times 8 =$ _____

27. $5 \times 5 =$ _____

28. $8 \times 5 =$ _____

29. $2 \times 6 =$ _____

30. $2 \times 2 =$ _____

31. $4 \times 7 =$ _____

32. $6 \times 7 =$ _____

33. $3 \times 6 =$ _____

34. $5 \times 9 =$ _____

35. $3 \times 8 =$ _____

36. $8 \times 6 =$ _____

37. $7 \times 2 =$ _____

38. $6 \times 8 =$ _____

39. $5 \times 7 =$ _____

40. $7 \times 3 =$ _____

41. $6 \times 6 =$ _____

42. $6 \times 5 =$ _____

43. $4 \times 4 =$ _____

44. $0 \times 2 =$ _____

45. $5 \times 4 =$ _____

46. $4 \times 9 =$ _____

47. $8 \times 3 =$ _____

48. $7 \times 9 =$ _____

49. $0 \times 4 =$ _____

50. $3 \times 7 =$ _____

Name_____

Give each answer.

1. $6 \times 3 =$ _____
2. $4 \times 7 =$ _____
3. $3 \times 7 =$ _____
4. $6 \times 6 =$ _____
5. $9 \times 5 =$ _____
6. $9 \times 4 =$ _____
7. $1 \times 7 =$ _____
8. $7 \times 2 =$ _____
9. $8 \times 8 =$ _____
10. $6 \times 1 =$ _____
11. $3 \times 2 =$ _____
12. $8 \times 9 =$ _____
13. $2 \times 6 =$ _____
14. $8 \times 6 =$ _____
15. $2 \times 2 =$ _____
16. $3 \times 5 =$ _____
17. $8 \times 2 =$ _____

18. $5 \times 5 =$ _____
19. $4 \times 9 =$ _____
20. $9 \times 3 =$ _____
21. $7 \times 8 =$ _____
22. $7 \times 5 =$ _____
23. $4 \times 5 =$ _____
24. $1 \times 1 =$ _____
25. $4 \times 3 =$ _____
26. $15 \div 5 =$ _____
27. $24 \div 8 =$ _____
28. $18 \div 2 =$ _____
29. $16 \div 2 =$ _____
30. $14 \div 2 =$ _____
31. $21 \div 3 =$ _____
32. $48 \div 6 =$ _____
33. $12 \div 2 =$ _____
34. $6 \div 1 =$ _____

35. $12 \div 3 =$ _____
36. $5 \div 5 =$ _____
37. $24 \div 4 =$ _____
38. $63 \div 7 =$ _____
39. $15 \div 3 =$ _____
40. $24 \div 3 =$ _____
41. $8 \div 2 =$ _____
42. $27 \div 9 =$ _____
43. $25 \div 5 =$ _____
44. $0 \div 1 =$ _____
45. $12 \div 4 =$ _____
46. $45 \div 5 =$ _____
47. $40 \div 8 =$ _____
48. $30 \div 5 =$ _____
49. $18 \div 6 =$ _____
50. $20 \div 4 =$ _____

Name_____

Give each answer.

1.	$16 \div 2 =$ _____	**18.**	$16 \div 4 =$ _____	**35.**	$18 \div 6 =$ _____
2.	$18 \div 2 =$ _____	**19.**	$45 \div 9 =$ _____	**36.**	$12 \div 4 =$ _____
3.	$12 \div 2 =$ _____	**20.**	$24 \div 8 =$ _____	**37.**	$18 \div 9 =$ _____
4.	$25 \div 5 =$ _____	**21.**	$63 \div 9 =$ _____	**38.**	$30 \div 5 =$ _____
5.	$24 \div 3 =$ _____	**22.**	$56 \div 7 =$ _____	**39.**	$9 \div 3 =$ _____
6.	$49 \div 7 =$ _____	**23.**	$24 \div 6 =$ _____	**40.**	$32 \div 4 =$ _____
7.	$28 \div 4 =$ _____	**24.**	$40 \div 8 =$ _____	**41.**	$45 \div 5 =$ _____
8.	$54 \div 6 =$ _____	**25.**	$30 \div 6 =$ _____	**42.**	$16 \div 8 =$ _____
9.	$10 \div 2 =$ _____	**26.**	$42 \div 6 =$ _____	**43.**	$28 \div 7 =$ _____
10.	$36 \div 9 =$ _____	**27.**	$15 \div 3 =$ _____	**44.**	$36 \div 4 =$ _____
11.	$27 \div 3 =$ _____	**28.**	$81 \div 9 =$ _____	**45.**	$7 \div 7 =$ _____
12.	$40 \div 8 =$ _____	**29.**	$15 \div 5 =$ _____	**46.**	$20 \div 5 =$ _____
13.	$35 \div 5 =$ _____	**30.**	$54 \div 9 =$ _____	**47.**	$10 \div 5 =$ _____
14.	$4 \div 2 =$ _____	**31.**	$6 \div 3 =$ _____	**48.**	$32 \div 8 =$ _____
15.	$6 \div 1 =$ _____	**32.**	$0 \div 2 =$ _____	**49.**	$42 \div 7 =$ _____
16.	$12 \div 6 =$ _____	**33.**	$48 \div 8 =$ _____	**50.**	$64 \div 8 =$ _____
17.	$72 \div 8 =$ _____	**34.**	$35 \div 7 =$ _____		

Name_____

Give each answer.

1. $15 \div 3 =$ _____
2. $24 \div 6 =$ _____
3. $5 \div 1 =$ _____
4. $16 \div 4 =$ _____
5. $4 \div 2 =$ _____
6. $35 \div 5 =$ _____
7. $12 \div 6 =$ _____
8. $18 \div 9 =$ _____
9. $28 \div 4 =$ _____
10. $12 \div 3 =$ _____
11. $36 \div 9 =$ _____
12. $25 \div 5 =$ _____
13. $8 \div 4 =$ _____
14. $30 \div 5 =$ _____
15. $36 \div 6 =$ _____
16. $35 \div 7 =$ _____
17. $9 \div 3 =$ _____

18. $0 \div 8 =$ _____
19. $6 \div 3 =$ _____
20. $63 \div 7 =$ _____
21. $56 \div 8 =$ _____
22. $12 \div 4 =$ _____
23. $30 \div 6 =$ _____
24. $64 \div 8 =$ _____
25. $20 \div 5 =$ _____
26. $21 \div 3 =$ _____
27. $45 \div 9 =$ _____
28. $24 \div 8 =$ _____
29. $27 \div 3 =$ _____
30. $40 \div 5 =$ _____
31. $49 \div 7 =$ _____
32. $54 \div 6 =$ _____
33. $21 \div 7 =$ _____
34. $6 \div 6 =$ _____

35. $72 \div 8 =$ _____
36. $4 \div 1 =$ _____
37. $36 \div 4 =$ _____
38. $63 \div 9 =$ _____
39. $8 \div 8 =$ _____
40. $48 \div 8 =$ _____
41. $45 \div 5 =$ _____
42. $72 \div 9 =$ _____
43. $0 \div 3 =$ _____
44. $14 \div 7 =$ _____
45. $81 \div 9 =$ _____
46. $56 \div 7 =$ _____
47. $32 \div 4 =$ _____
48. $18 \div 3 =$ _____
49. $42 \div 6 =$ _____
50. $40 \div 8 =$ _____

Name_____

Give each answer.

1. $5 \times 6 =$ _____

2. $4 \times 8 =$ _____

3. $9 \times 1 =$ _____

4. $7 \times 8 =$ _____

5. $3 \times 9 =$ _____

6. $7 \times 3 =$ _____

7. $9 \times 9 =$ _____

8. $2 \times 8 =$ _____

9. $9 \times 5 =$ _____

10. $5 \times 8 =$ _____

11. $1 \times 9 =$ _____

12. $9 \times 7 =$ _____

13. $3 \times 5 =$ _____

14. $8 \times 8 =$ _____

15. $7 \times 6 =$ _____

16. $8 \times 3 =$ _____

17. $2 \times 2 =$ _____

18. $4 \times 7 =$ _____

19. $6 \times 9 =$ _____

20. $4 \times 3 =$ _____

21. $4 \times 5 =$ _____

22. $7 \times 5 =$ _____

23. $5 \times 1 =$ _____

24. $7 \times 7 =$ _____

25. $6 \times 4 =$ _____

26. $16 \div 2 =$ _____

27. $8 \div 2 =$ _____

28. $20 \div 4 =$ _____

29. $4 \div 4 =$ _____

30. $14 \div 2 =$ _____

31. $10 \div 5 =$ _____

32. $18 \div 3 =$ _____

33. $14 \div 7 =$ _____

34. $6 \div 2 =$ _____

35. $9 \div 3 =$ _____

36. $8 \div 1 =$ _____

37. $5 \div 5 =$ _____

38. $35 \div 5 =$ _____

39. $24 \div 6 =$ _____

40. $21 \div 3 =$ _____

41. $27 \div 9 =$ _____

42. $56 \div 8 =$ _____

43. $30 \div 6 =$ _____

44. $8 \div 4 =$ _____

45. $10 \div 2 =$ _____

46. $16 \div 8 =$ _____

47. $12 \div 3 =$ _____

48. $42 \div 7 =$ _____

49. $45 \div 9 =$ _____

50. $18 \div 2 =$ _____

Name_____

Give each answer.

1. $3 + 5 =$ _____

2. $9 + 1 =$ _____

3. $4 + 7 =$ _____

4. $5 - 2 =$ _____

5. $8 - 0 =$ _____

6. $8 - 3 =$ _____

7. $3 + 4 =$ _____

8. $5 + 6 =$ _____

9. $7 + 9 =$ _____

10. $12 - 5 =$ _____

11. $7 - 3 =$ _____

12. $4 + 4 =$ _____

13. $2 + 6 =$ _____

14. $10 - 9 =$ _____

15. $2 + 4 =$ _____

16. $5 + 8 =$ _____

17. $14 - 6 =$ _____

18. $4 - 2 =$ _____

19. $5 + 1 =$ _____

20. $13 - 4 =$ _____

21. $6 + 7 =$ _____

22. $3 + 8 =$ _____

23. $4 - 1 =$ _____

24. $15 - 8 =$ _____

25. $6 + 9 =$ _____

26. $5 - 1 =$ _____

27. $9 - 5 =$ _____

28. $8 + 7 =$ _____

29. $6 + 4 =$ _____

30. $10 - 2 =$ _____

31. $18 - 9 =$ _____

32. $3 + 9 =$ _____

33. $5 + 4 =$ _____

34. $11 - 2 =$ _____

35. $5 + 7 =$ _____

36. $14 - 9 =$ _____

37. $15 - 6 =$ _____

38. $12 - 7 =$ _____

39. $4 + 8 =$ _____

40. $3 + 7 =$ _____

41. $14 - 8 =$ _____

42. $6 + 3 =$ _____

43. $7 + 7 =$ _____

44. $16 - 7 =$ _____

45. $10 - 5 =$ _____

46. $5 + 9 =$ _____

47. $11 - 4 =$ _____

48. $13 - 9 =$ _____

49. $7 + 8 =$ _____

50. $17 - 8 =$ _____

Name_____

Give each answer.

1. $8 + 3 =$ ____

2. $3 + 2 =$ ____

3. $8 + 7 =$ ____

4. $8 + 9 =$ ____

5. $1 + 5 =$ ____

6. $9 + 0 =$ ____

7. $13 - 6 =$ ____

8. $9 - 9 =$ ____

9. $9 - 4 =$ ____

10. $11 - 9 =$ ____

11. $14 - 7 =$ ____

12. $13 - 8 =$ ____

13. $5 + 2 =$ ____

14. $7 + 6 =$ ____

15. $8 - 2 =$ ____

16. $15 - 7 =$ ____

17. $3 + 7 =$ ____

18. $6 - 3 =$ ____

19. $4 + 2 =$ ____

20. $4 + 9 =$ ____

21. $11 - 7 =$ ____

22. $5 + 3 =$ ____

23. $7 - 5 =$ ____

24. $6 - 0 =$ ____

25. $1 + 1 =$ ____

26. $7 \times 4 =$ ____

27. $5 \times 3 =$ ____

28. $2 \times 4 =$ ____

29. $6 \times 8 =$ ____

30. $3 \times 7 =$ ____

31. $7 \times 9 =$ ____

32. $7 \times 7 =$ ____

33. $4 \times 8 =$ ____

34. $4 \times 2 =$ ____

35. $1 \times 8 =$ ____

36. $4 \times 4 =$ ____

37. $5 \times 8 =$ ____

38. $2 \times 5 =$ ____

39. $6 \div 2 =$ ____

40. $18 \div 3 =$ ____

41. $9 \div 9 =$ ____

42. $32 \div 4 =$ ____

43. $16 \div 4 =$ ____

44. $10 \div 2 =$ ____

45. $20 \div 5 =$ ____

46. $48 \div 6 =$ ____

47. $63 \div 9 =$ ____

48. $14 \div 7 =$ ____

49. $64 \div 8 =$ ____

50. $9 \div 1 =$ ____

Name_____

Give each answer.

1. 4 + 6 = _____

2. 9 + 3 = _____

3. 1 + 4 = _____

4. 7 + 4 = _____

5. 0 + 0 = _____

6. 15 − 7 = _____

7. 11 − 7 = _____

8. 16 − 8 = _____

9. 1 + 6 = _____

10. 14 − 6 = _____

11. 9 − 9 = _____

12. 12 − 4 = _____

13. 7 + 5 = _____

14. 9 + 5 = _____

15. 3 − 1 = _____

16. 3 + 6 = _____

17. 11 − 7 = _____

18. 4 + 1 = _____

19. 8 − 3 = _____

20. 9 − 7 = _____

21. 9 + 9 = _____

22. 9 + 7 = _____

23. 4 − 1 = _____

24. 7 − 6 = _____

25. 3 + 1 = _____

26. 2 × 3 = _____

27. 6 × 4 = _____

28. 6 × 8 = _____

29. 4 × 6 = _____

30. 8 × 2 = _____

31. 1 × 2 = _____

32. 5 × 2 = _____

33. 9 × 9 = _____

34. 4 × 4 = _____

35. 6 × 7 = _____

36. 1 × 6 = _____

37. 2 × 4 = _____

38. 8 × 7 = _____

39. 6 ÷ 3 = _____

40. 27 ÷ 3 = _____

41. 32 ÷ 8 = _____

42. 24 ÷ 4 = _____

43. 12 ÷ 2 = _____

44. 18 ÷ 9 = _____

45. 48 ÷ 6 = _____

46. 28 ÷ 7 = _____

47. 36 ÷ 4 = _____

48. 3 ÷ 1 = _____

49. 54 ÷ 9 = _____

50. 72 ÷ 8 = _____